Nuclear Transmutation:
The Reality of Cold Fusion

Nuclear Transmutation: The Reality of Cold Fusion

by Dr. Tadahiko Mizuno
Department of Nuclear Engineering
Hokkaido University, Japan

Translation and Introduction
by Jed Rothwell

Infinite Energy Press
Concord, New Hampshire, U.S.A.

With a Foreword
by Eugene F. Mallove, Sc. D.

Originally published in Japanese as *Nuclear Transmutation - the Reality of Cold Fusion,* Kogakusha, Copyright © 1997

Infinite Energy Press, P.O. Box 2816, Concord, NH 03302-2816
English translation Copyright © 1998

Printed in the United States of America.

Library of Congress Catalog Card Number: 98-88307
Mizuno, Tadahiko
   [Nuclear Transmutation: The Reality of Cold Fusion. English]
   (Translated by Jed Rothwell)
   Includes bibliographical references.
   Includes index.
   ISBN 1-892925-00-1

Text design by Barbara A.F. DelloRusso
Set in 11-point Garamond by Agfa

This book is printed on acid-free paper.

Find us on the World Wide Web at: http://www.infinite-energy.com

CONTENTS

FOREWORD

When a scientific discovery seems to break all the rules, when it appears to violate cherished theories held for decades or hundreds of years, it breaks a fundamental paradigm and there is hell to pay. Such is the case in the scientific revolution that began on March 23, 1989, when electrochemists Drs. Martin Fleischmann and Stanley Pons announced "cold fusion" at a press conference at the University of Utah.

In the history of science there will be few peaks higher or stranger than the discovery of cold fusion. From that moment, a long-held notion was to be smashed forever: that atoms could not change their nuclear identities in near-room temperature reactions—reactions that were presumed to be chemical, not nuclear. Following the Fleischmann-Pons announcement, intense scientific investigations in electrochemistry uncovered a whole new class of low-temperature nuclear reactions. The astounding claims of Fleischmann and Pons had involved primarily large excess energy production, but also tritium formation and the appearance of low levels of neutrons. Later, investigators began to observe heavier elements and strange isotopes that were not present when their experiments began. Even "mainstream" cold fusion researchers, who focused on helium-production as the long sought "nuclear ash" of the cold fusion fire, found it difficult to accept the accelerating research on the low-energy transmutation of heavy elements.

It is now clear that Fleischmann and Pons discovered the mere tip of an iceberg within physics and chemistry. This new realm may eventually be called electro-nuclear reactions, so encompassing has it become. It was not merely a new "island" of physics that had come into view, but a whole new continent. Other names have been put forward for these alchemy-like reactions: "chemically assisted nuclear reactions" or LENRs (low energy nuclear reactions). Whatever the name, it seems that twentieth century physics took a wrong turn long ago by denying that such reactions could occur. There may be an error in the foundations of physics. Either that or quantum mechanicians will have to do very fancy footwork to explain what is happening in a provocative variety of cold fusion experiments.

It took a long time to verify the primary claim of Fleischmann and Pons, that an electrochemical cell with heavy water electrolyte and a palladium cathode could produce excess energy orders of magnitude beyond chemical reactions. Their announcement could have been a mistake—and the uninformed or those who rushed to judgment still think it is—but it was no mistake. Peer-reviewed and non-peer-reviewed scientific literature rule that out. "Cold fusion"—whatever its ultimate microphysical explanation turns out to be—accomplishes two "miracles": 1) Highly positively charged nuclei of atoms which strongly repel each other are made to effect nuclear reactions at temperatures a million-fold cooler than in the cores of stars; and 2) When these reactions occur, they do not produce deadly radiation.

Dr. Tadahiko Mizuno, the electrochemist author of this extraordinary book is one of the eminent cold fusion pioneers. He tells the story of how he came into the field and how he determined for himself whether cold fusion was real or a mistake. In the process, we learn much about the methods of science and about the day-to-day work of a cold fusion scientist working on the frontiers of knowledge. We also learn about the political storms that erupted as the reigning scientific paradigm that separated chemistry from nuclear physics began to collapse.

I started investigating cold fusion on March 23, 1989 as a trained engineer who had moved into science journalism. I had never encountered a scientific revolution first hand. Prior to that, my acquaintance with scientific revolution came from history books. I was not prepared for the politics and human failings that attended the assaults against cold fusion by the scientific establishment, and especially by thermonuclear researchers at my alma mater, MIT, where I was at the time. It took a year for me to conclude that the evidence was mounting strongly in favor of the phenomenon. When my book, *Fire from Ice: Searching for the Truth Behind the Cold Fusion Furor* came out (1991, John Wiley & Sons), I concluded that the evidence was overwhelmingly compelling for cold fusion being a real, but still unexplained nuclear-related process. The science and early technological commercial ventures in the field have ratified this conclusion.

That has not stopped attacks against the field by those who continue to ignore solid experimental evidence in favor of old theories that presume to "prove" that low energy nuclear reactions are impossible. One of the most remarkable opinions came from physics professor Herman Feshbach of MIT, who angrily told me in 1991: "I have had fifty years of experience in nuclear physics and I know what is possible and what is impossible...I do not want to look at any more evidence for cold fusion. It's all junk!" Yes, Galileo, we will not look through your telescope! As science and truth win out, it is possible that some of the less committed skeptics will have second thoughts about their past dogmatic beliefs—perhaps by reading Dr. Mizuno's fascinating first-person account. We fervently hope so.

The evidence before us has become mountainous. It is no longer "overwhelmingly compelling"; it is now certain. We now know that the oceans, lakes, rivers, and streams of the world can be virtually infinite sources of clean and inexpensive energy for humankind. Locked in the structure of various forms of hydrogen in contact with special materials are fantastic energies. Genie-like, they remained hidden for the thousands of years that human beings trod this planet and revered water as the source and sustenance of life. We have found them and they are ours—if we have the wisdom to use them.

Eugene F. Mallove, Sc.D.
Editor-in-Chief
Infinite Energy Magazine

ACKNOWLEDGMENTS

I am indebted to many people, and many organizations and corporations for assistance in this research. I mentioned Masao Araki in Chapter 5. I would like to thank others for help in preparing and analyzing materials: Kimio Ishimaru of the Osaka Gas Company Ltd., Susumu Ushigome and Yajima Tamotsu of TYK Ltd., Susumu Sawada of Japan Energy Ltd., Yoshiyuki Kashiwagi of Meidenshya Ltd., Hidehiko Tajima of Mitsubishi Heavy Industry Co., Keji Kunimatsu of IMRA Japan Ltd., Kenya Mori of Tanaka Precious Metal Co. Ltd., Toshinori Shigemitsu of Nuclear Fuel Material Co. For discussions and information I thank Fujio Nakano, Jed Rothwell and Shigejo Shimokawa.

Editorial Acknowledgments (Infinite Energy Press) for the English translation: For assistance in editing the translation and many helpful suggestions, I thank Jed Rothwell, Susan Seddon, and Eugene Mallove. For production, I thank Barbara DelloRusso, managing editor and text designer; cover graphics, Jeremy Slayton; and proofreading, Christy Frazier.

I would like to express profound gratitude to all.

Tadahiko Mizuno
Hokkaido National University, Sapporo, 1997

PREFACE

It was nine years ago, in March of 1989. In America, electrochemists Martin Fleischmann and Stanley Pons announced they had achieved "low temperature deuterium nuclear fusion with electrochemical methods," in other words, cold fusion. They said that when heavy water was decomposed with palladium and platinum electrodes a large amount of excess heat was produced. If true, this would be the "ultimate energy source." There would be no point in bothering with plasma fusion development, which has continued for decades without break-even results.

After the announcement, researchers worldwide attempted to come to grips with cold fusion, but they reported they were not even able to replicate the effect, to say nothing of controlling it or explaining the mechanism.

In a few experiments, there were definite signs of neutrons and tritium production, and excess heat was observed. That's not all. It seems the real cause of these effects is not merely nuclear fusion after all. Rather, it is nuclear "transmutation," the conversion of heavy elements into other elements, by fission and fusion. Some people might dismiss the whole ideas as alchemy. In a sense, alchemy is exactly what it is. But it is not that simple. I ask the reader to examine the evidence in this book carefully, for within it we find that an unexpected new world has been revealed.

Tadahiko Mizuno
Hokkaido National University, Sapporo, 1997
(As translated from the Japanese Edition)

INTRODUCTION

The announcement of cold fusion in March 1989 at the University of Utah was greeted with worldwide hysteria. Drs. Martin Fleischmann and Stanley Pons had claimed that an electrochemical cell with heavy water electrolyte and a palladium cathode put out so much excess energy that the mysterious phenomenon had to be nuclear, and was probably a process related to nuclear fusion. Newspapers and magazines said it might be a major scientific discovery with the potential to end the energy crisis and revolutionize society. For a few heady months the public took it seriously and waited anxiously for laboratories to replicate the results. Many scientists quickly took sides for or against cold fusion—mostly against. Then, by the end of the summer of 1989 the official word came, in the draft of an authoritative report written by a select panel of experts under the auspices of the Department of Energy: cold fusion was a bust. It did not exist. It was an experimental error. It could not be reproduced. Nearly every scientific journal, magazine and newspaper on earth reported this, and cold fusion abruptly dropped out of the headlines. The story, it seemed, was over. Actually, it had barely begun. Only a few thousand electrochemists in the world were qualified to do the experiments, and most of them were too busy or not interested in trying. In that autumn as public interest faded and the U.S. Department of Energy pronounced a death sentence with its final report, a small number of experienced scientists prepared serious, full-scale experiments. One of them was Tadahiko Mizuno, an assistant professor who had been doing similar electrochemical experiments for more than twenty years.

Mizuno wrote this short book about his work and personal experiences. It is the best informal account yet written about the daily life of a cold fusion researcher. It gives you a sense of what the job feels like. It is not intended to be technical. For technical details, the reader is invited to examine Mizuno's numerous scientific papers. See references and appendices.

One event described here which is not mentioned in the technical literature is an extraordinary ten-day long heat-after-death incident that occurred in 1991. News of this appeared in the popular press,* but a formal description was never published in a scientific paper. Mizuno says this is because

*F. Nakano, "Mohaya hitei dekinai jyouon kakuyuugou [The reality of cold fusion can no longer be denied]," Bungei Shunju, September 1991]

he does not have carefully established calorimetric data to prove the event occurred, but I think he does not need it. The cell went out of control. Mizuno cooled it over ten days by placing it in a large bucket of water. During this period, more than 37 liters of water evaporated from the bucket, which means the cell produced more than 84 megajoules of energy during this period alone, and 114 megajoules during the entire experiment. The only active material in the cell was 100 grams of palladium. It produced 27 times more energy than an equivalent mass of the best chemical fuel (gasoline) can produce. I think the 36 liters of evaporated water constitute better scientific evidence than the most carefully calibrated high precision instrument could produce. This is first principle proof of heat. A bucket left by itself for ten days in a university laboratory will not lose any significant level of water to evaporation. First principle experiments are not fashionable. Many scientists nowadays will not look at a simple experiment in which 36 liters of water evaporate, but high tech instruments and computers are not used. They will dismiss this as "anecdotal evidence."

It is a terrible shame that Mizuno did not call in a dozen other scientists to see and feel the hot cell. I would have set up a 24-hour vigil with graduate students and video cameras to observe the cell and measure the evaporated water carefully. This is one of history's heartbreaking lost opportunities. News of this event, properly documented and attested to by many people, might have convinced thousands of scientists worldwide that cold fusion is real. This might have been one of the most effective scientific demonstrations in history. Unfortunately, it occurred during an extended national holiday, and Mizuno decided to disconnect the cell from the recording equipment and hide it in his laboratory. He placed it behind a steel sheet because he was afraid it might explode. He told me he was not anxious to have the cell certified by many other people because he thought that he would soon replicate the effect in another experiment. Alas, in the seven years since, neither he nor any other scientist has ever seen such dramatic, inarguable proof of massive excess energy in a cold fusion experiment.

Here is a chronology of the heat-after-death event:

March 1991: A new experiment with the closed cell begins.
April 1991: Cell shows small but significant excess heat.
April 22: 1991. Electrolysis stopped.
April 25: Mizuno and Akimoto note that temperature is elevated.
It has produced 1.2×10^7 joules since April 22, in heat-after-death.

The cell is removed from the underground lab and transferred to Mizuno's lab. Cell temperature is >100°C.

April 26: Cell temperature has not declined. Cell transferred to a 15-liter bucket, where it is partially submerged in water.

April 27: Most of the water in the bucket, ~10 liters, has evaporated.

The cell is transferred to a larger, 20 liter bucket. It is fully submerged in 15 liters of water.

April 30: Most of the water has evaporated; ~10 liters.

More water is added to the bucket, bringing the total to 15 liters again.

May 1: 5 liters of water are added to the bucket.

May 2: Five more liters are added to the bucket.

May 7: The cell is finally cool. 7.5 liters of water remain in the bucket.

Total evaporation equals:

April 27: 10 liters evaporated. Water level set at 15 liters in a new bucket.

April 30: 10 liters evaporated. Water replenished to 15 liters.

May 1: 5 liters replenished.

May 2: 5 liters replenished.

May 7: 7.5 liters remaining.

Thus, evaporation since April 30 is: 15+5+5-7.5=17.5 liters. Total evaporation is 37.5 liters. The heat of vaporization of water is 540 calories per gram (2,268 joules per gram), so vaporization alone accounts for 85 megajoules.

One aspect of the heat-after-death event seems particularly strange. It is as if the cathode is trying to maintain stasis inside the cell. After the external 60 watt heater was turned off, the heat-after-death reaction increased just about enough to compensate for the loss of external heat. This sounds like an instrument error. It prompted Mizuno to double check all instrument readings with meters attached directly to the sensors. As unbelievable as this sounds, it is a real phenomenon which others have observed. Stanley Pons noted that the cold fusion effect has a kind of "memory." After a perturbation, temperature tends to return to a fixed level. Perhaps this is not so strange. The physical configuration of deuterons in the metal controls the power level. Tiny spots in the surface of the cathode are probably formed in what Edmund Storms of Los Alamos National Laboratory calls "a special configuration of matter" with highly active, densely packed deuterium. Until these spots change or disperse, the nuclear fuel being fed into the reaction remains constant, so the cell tends to return to the same power level. A chemical wood fire works the same way. You can partially douse a roaring fire. If the fire does not go out altogether and the wood remains in the same position, after a while it will start burning again and return to its former power level. Pons and Fleischmann used a three-minute pulse of heat to "kick" their cells from low level heat to the high level heat that rapidly increased to boil off. The heat was generated by joule heating (resistor heating) from externally supplied power, but once the cathode was boosted into higher activity the external power could be withdrawn and the cathode continued to self-heat—thus "heat-after-death."

Metal undergoing cold fusion "wants" to be hot and will keep itself hot, prolonging the reaction. When Mizuno put his cell in the bucket of water the reaction began to turn off, presumably because the water in the bucket cooled the cathode. It did not quench the reaction immediately because the cathode was fairly well insulated inside a large thermal mass. Later, the water in the bucket warmed up well above room temperature; 10 liters of it evaporated, leaving the cell surrounded by air. The cell began to self heat again and it returned to its previously high level of activity. Storms thinks that in the special configuration, the deuterium diffusion rate is slower at high temperatures than usual. Normal beta-phase palladium deuteride will de-gas more rapidly when it heats up. He thinks that when the temperature falls (or is lowered by a thermal shock), the deuteride converts to beta-phase and begins rapidly de-gassing, and the cold fusion effect goes away.

Mizuno has often talked about the prehistory of cold fusion. Most great discoveries are visited and revisited many times before someone stakes a permanent claim. People sometimes stumble over a new discovery without even realizing what they see. Mizuno did his graduate and post-graduate work on corrosion using highly loaded metal hydrides. His experiments were almost exactly like those of cold fusion, but they were performed for a different purpose. In retrospect, he realized that he saw anomalous events that may have been cold fusion. At the time he could not determine the cause, he did not imagine it might be fusion, and he had to leave the mystery unsolved. No scientist has time to track down every anomaly. I expect many people saw and disregarded evidence for cold fusion over the years. Mizuno makes a provocative assertion. He says that long before 1989 he wondered whether the immense pressure of electrolysis might produce "some form of fusion." He says: "This kind of hypothesis would occur to any researcher studying metal and hydrogen systems. It is not a particularly profound or outstanding idea. It never occurred to me to pursue the matter and research this further." He appears to downplay the role of Pons and Fleischmann. Perhaps he exaggerates when he says "any researcher" would think of it, but on the other hand Paneth and Peters and others did investigate this topic in the 1920s.

It has been floating around the literature for a long time. Pons and Fleischmann deserve credit because they did more than merely speculate about it. They succeeded in doing the experiments to prove it. Perhaps cold fusion is self-evident in the way that many great discoveries are. An ordinary genius finds an obscure and difficult truth which remains obscure even after he publishes, except to other experts. A superlative genius makes a discovery that few other people imagined, yet which everyone later agrees is obvious in retrospect. When T.H. Huxley learned of the theory of natural selection, he reportedly exclaimed: "Why didn't I think of that!"

Within days of the 1989 announcement, Mizuno set to work on a "crude, preliminary" experiment. He built the cell in a single afternoon, which is in itself astonishing. His purpose was to detect neutrons, which he along with everyone else in 1989 assumed would be the principal signature of the reaction. Months later it became clear that heat is the principal signature and neutrons appear sporadically. The neutron flux is a million times smaller in proportion to the heat than it is with hot fusion. His colleague Akimoto, an expert in neutron detection, soon convinced him that the instrumentation must be improved and the cell must be moved to a well-shielded location before meaningful results might be obtained. The underground laboratory housing the linear accelerator, close by on campus, was the ideal spot for the experiment, but it is hardly an ideal place for people. It is dark, dank, and unheated in winter, as Mizuno well knew from years of doing graduate research there. After weeks of operation, the experiment showed slight signs of generating 2.45 MeV neutrons. Mizuno decided to get serious.

Here we learn what a real scientist is made of. While the rest of the world rushed to judgement, Mizuno buckled down and began a second "serious" experiment. The preparations took eight months. Mizuno and a graduate student worked long days building and testing the cell, and preparing the anode, cathode, electrolyte, and controls. They planned to run at 100°C and 10 atmospheres of pressure, so they ran pressure tests at 150°C and 50 atmospheres, improving the seals and connections until they saw no significant pressure decline for days. Finally they were ready to begin the first test run. The hysteria was long past. The press and the establishment had dismissed cold fusion. Real experiments by people like Mizuno were getting underway. When these tests were finished and documented, a year or two later, they constituted definitive proof of tritium, excess heat, helium, and transmutation. It is tempting to think that the tragedy of cold fusion boils down to—a short attention span. If only *Nature*, the newspapers, the DoE and the American Physical Society understood that you cannot do a research project in a few weeks, they would have withheld judgement until Mizuno, Fritz Will, Melvin Miles and others published in 1990 and 1991.

In person, Mizuno is charming, self-deprecating, optimistic and brimming with ideas. In this book he describes the dark side of the story: the frustration, the boredom, the endless guerrilla war with scientists who wanted to stop the research, and science journalists who appeared to thrive on the outpouring of supposedly negative results, and the fruitless battles to publish a paper or be heard at a physics conference. Research means years of hard work which must often be done in appalling circumstances: in an unheated underground laboratory, late at night, in Hokkaido's Siberian climate. Experiments must be tended to four times a day, from eight in the morning until eight at night, seven days a week, without a holiday or a weekend off. He describes these travails, but he does not dwell on them, or the controversy and politics. He revels in the fun parts of cold fusion: the discovery, the sense of wonder, the rewards. Mizuno does not waste his time moping or worrying. He gets to work, he does experiments, he teaches and encourages students. The first 5,000 copy printing of this book sold out quickly in Japan. Mizuno was thrilled because, he told me, "undergrads are buying it, and calling me with questions." He and I wanted to move the Sixth International Conference on Cold Fusion (ICCF-6) out of the isolated mountaintop resort hotel in Hokkaido, back to the city of Sapporo, and into the grubby Student Union meeting hall on campus. If we had been in charge, we would have opened up the conference and allowed free admission to students. We think that when engineering and physics majors drift into such conferences and realize what is happening, cold fusion will take off.

Despite the troubles, Mizuno remains confident that we will succeed in the end. The research will be allowed, papers will be published, rapid progress will be made. Others, like Fleischmann, are deeply pessimistic. Some of the best scientists in this field, including Storms, are deeply discouraged by the constant struggle and expense. They sometimes tell me they are on the verge of quitting. But Mizuno has never flagged, never doubted, and never lost hope. As Storms says, "We must have hope. We have no other resources in this field."

Mizuno wants to make practical devices. He wants to improve reproducibility and scale up. He talks about the scientist's obligation to give society something of value. He and Dennis Cravens are the only cold fusion scientists I know who say that openly. He succeeded in replicating the original Pons and Fleischmann palladium cold fusion in three experiments, but it was difficult and the reaction proved impossible to control, so he did not see much future in it. Instead of trying to improve the original experiment by repeating it many times with minor variations, the way McKubre, Kunimatsu and others have attempted, Mizuno decided to try other materials and other approaches.* He is a one-man R&D consortium. Some may criticize him for trying too many things and spreading himself too thinly. As I see it, Mizuno is doing his share. The rest of the world is to blame for not following his lead. He worked on ceramic proton conductors for years, he published detailed information in professional, full-length papers, and he assisted Oriani by fabricating a batch of conductors (a week of difficult labor on Oriani's behalf).** No other scientist has been as cooperative, willing to share data, and willing to assist others replicate. If Mizuno has left jobs unfinished, others should have taken up these jobs.

Mizuno concentrates on the rewards, the progress, the heady sense of excitement, the breathtaking possibilities. If progress has been slow, it has been real, and the scope of the research has broadened immeasurably. In 1989 we thought we had stumbled onto one isolated uncharted island. It turned out we have discovered a whole new continent. No wonder our exploration of it is taking longer than we expected. Over the years I have asked many scientists where cold fusion may be taking us and how big the discovery might be. Only Martin Fleischmann has shown a deep under-standing of how many ramifications it may have.

Mizuno describes few moments of epiphany. There are moments of excite-ment, but most of the triumphs are long expected, and a good result does not mean much until you make it happen again, and again after that. There are few revelations. The scientists do not suddenly grasp the answer. They gradually narrow down a set of possibilities. Often the same possibilities are examined, discounted, and then reconsidered years later. Recently, Mizuno, Bockris and others have increasingly focused on so-called "host metal trans-mutations," that is, nuclear reactions of the cathode metal itself. The cath-ode metal was inexplicably neglected for many years. The term "host metal" is misleading. It was an unfortunate choice of words. It implies that the metal acts as a passive structure, holding the hydrogen in place, cramming the deuterons or protons together. The metal is a host, not a participant. The hydrogen does the work. Now, it appears the metal itself is as active as the hydrogen. The metal apparently fissions and fusions in complex reactions. Now the task is to think about the metal, and not just the hydrogen. Theory must explain how palladium can be partially transmuted into copper and other elements with peculiar isotopes.

One of the few "Eureka!" events in this book is the moment when Mizuno and Ohmori saw the scanning electron microscope images of the

*Dr. Michael C. McKubre, SRI International, Menlo Park, California; Dr.. Keiji Kunimatsu, IMRA Europe, Sophia Antipolis, France
**Prof. Richard A. Oriani, University of Minnesota, Minneapolis, Minnesota

beautiful lily-shaped eruptions on the surface of Ohmori's gold cathodes.[*] This was visual proof that a violent reaction takes place under the surface of the metal, vaporizing the metal and spewing it out. Later, these vaporized spots were found to be the locus of transmutation. Around them are gathered elements with an isotopic distribution that does not exist in nature. The only likely explanation is that these isotopes are the product of a nuclear transmutation.

Mizuno describes the wrong directions he has taken, the dead ends, the mistakes. For years he ignored the most important clue: the host metal transmutations. He did not check the composition of the used cathodes. After his first big success produced tritium and spectacular heat-after-death, he opened the cell to find the cathode was blackened by something. He thought it must be contamination, and he was disappointed that his painstaking efforts to exclude contamination had failed. After puzzling over it for a long time he scraped the black film off the cathode with glass, and prepared the cathode for another run. Years later he realized that this black film was probably formed from microscopic erupted structures similar to those on Ohmori's cathodes. He says in retrospect he was throwing away treasure. Even Mizuno, an open minded, observant and perceptive scientist, has to be hit over the head with the same evidence many times before he realizes it is crucial. Other people are worse. Mizuno was blind for a long time; other cold fusion scientists remain blind to this day. They are unwilling to do simple tests that might reveal the nature of the reaction. IMRA,[**] the Toyota laboratory where Fleischmann and Pons did their research, is a sad example. Informed sources say IMRA researchers never performed an autoradiograph on a used cathode.

A recurring theme in this book is money. Mizuno frets, schemes and struggles to reduce expenses. He worries about the consumption of heavy water at $8 or $10 per day. He does not reveal in the book why these trivial expenses bother him so much: most of the money comes out of his own pocket. University discretionary funding allotted to professors in Japan does not begin to cover the expense of cold fusion research. It would be called "noise level funding" in the U.S., or "sparrow's tears" in the Japanese idiom. Most of the other professors at Hokkaido remain hostile toward this research, and unwilling to allocate more money for it, so Mizuno often pays for equipment, materials, travel expenses and so on himself. Over the years the research has cost him tens of thousands of dollars, which is a great deal of money for a middle-class Japanese family. Cold

---

[*]Dr. Tadayoshi Ohmori, Catalysis Research Center, Hokkaido University, Japan
[**]IMRA Japan Co. Ltd., Sapporo, Japan

fusion research consumes a constant flow of new equipment. The Japanese scientific establishment and the university barely tolerate this research. Still, Mizuno is better off than he would be at most U.S. universities, which have essentially banned this research.

Mizuno describes the dank, underground laboratory. He does not mention that his own laboratory is the size of a broom closet and so crammed with equipment you can barely fit in the door. The roof leaks. A large sheet of blue plastic is suspended over the corner of the room, funneling the rain water down to a sink and away from the computers, meters, power supplies and complex, delicate, beautiful handcrafted experimental apparatus, made of aluminum, stainless steel, platinum, gold and silver.

Jed Rothwell
Atlanta, Georgia 1998

NOTES ON EXCHANGE RATES AND THE TRANSLATION

During the period this book covers, one dollar was worth between 90 and 120 yen. The heavy water described in Chapter Three cost $130 every two weeks, and the platinum recombiner described in Chapter 4 with the "sky high" price of 200,000 yen equals about $2,000. That may not seem like much for research which might end the energy crisis and the threat of global warming, but it is a lot of money for a professor to pay out of his own pocket.

This translation is based on a book published by Kogakusha in 1997. Mizuno sent me his original manuscript in Japanese via e-mail. The version he sent was longer than the book. The Japanese publisher cut some technical details to make it easier for the general reader, and cut many sarcastic and controversial comments. I was pleased to put both back into the English version.

Japanese language textbooks often advise: "pronounce the consonants as in English and the vowels as in Italian." *

In Japanese, people's names are written surname first: Mizuno Tadahiko, Sato Norio. To avoid confusion, I have put them in English order: Tadahiko Mizuno, Norio Sato (given name, surname).

The title of this book in Japanese is "Kakuhenkan - jyouon kakuyuugou no shinjitsu," which I have rendered: Nuclear Transmutation - The Reality of Cold Fusion. The word "shinjitsu" (reality) also means "truth," so the subtitle might be rendered: "What Cold Fusion Really Is."

*S. E. Martin, A Reference Grammar of Japanese, (Tuttle, 1988)

Trial and error exploration, which is sometimes like walking through a pitch dark room, gradually leads to results, which shape theories, which in turn corroborate experiments. From this cycle of routine, modest toil— experiments, theory, more experiments—science finally reveals splendid truths.

Tadahiko Mizuno

1

PROLOGUE

The First International Low Energy Nuclear Reactions Conference

It was June 17, 1995, two days before the First International Low Energy Nuclear Reactions Conference. I was looking out of the window of a small airplane at night as I flew over the broad vistas of Texas from Dallas to College Station. I was thinking about my experiences more than a decade earlier.

In July 1983 Professor Norio Sato of the Hokkaido University Engineering Department suggested that I apply to do postdoctorate research overseas, at the chemistry department of Texas A&M University under Professor John Bockris (See Plate 20). At the time, Bockris, a famous electrochemist, was in his mid-sixties and still in high spirits. He was born in South Africa and graduated from the University of London. He is an expert in corrosion and corrosion prevention, the conversion of light to electricity (photovoltaics), organic battery chemistry, and many other areas.

Sato was also a famous electrochemist, specializing in advanced research in passive films. He had known Bockris for many years.

There were some twenty postdoctoral positions in Bockris' lab, filled with exceptional students from all over the world.

In March of 1984, on the day I arrived at Texas A&M, Bockris and I met for two hours to discuss the research I would undertake.

The workload was frightful. I used infrared spectroscopy to analyze electrochemical reactions on metal surfaces, and a radiochemical method with a

Figure 1.
Texas A&M
University

beta source to measure the absorption of ions on the electrode at anodic and cathodic regions. I worked for weeks without a day off. I was three times busier than I had been in Japan.

In the U.S., all research has to be funded by outside sponsors. Professors are rated by their ability to attract funding. In Japan, at a national university ten years ago, you did not have to do anything in particular to get funding (albeit, only a pittance). Every year you would get your share of funding no matter what. But the budget has not been increased in years, and with that money alone it is utterly impossible to do any real research. You have to appeal for a grant from industry or a foundation. I think in this respect Japan has become more like the U.S. I myself do not think this system is especially desirable, but on the other hand the old system of entitlements had its drawbacks too. In any case, Bockris was one of the dominant figures in electrochemistry who attracted big funding.

The conference got underway on June 19, 1995 (Monday), at 8:30 in the morning in a newly refurbished meeting hall in the chemistry department at Texas A&M. Bockris opened the meeting with a spirited discussion of the purposes of the conference. He outlined the developments that had led up to it, and the momentous changes he envisaged that lay in store for the field. Participants numbered about 50, with 16 people scheduled to give papers. Bockris sat at the front row of the meeting hall, directing the meeting, expediting the presentations and chairing the question and answer sessions.

I was scheduled to give a talk at 2:50 in the afternoon. My thirty minutes swept by in no time. Before I had a chance to say half of what I planned, Bockris was warning me I had "a few more minutes left." I somehow managed to wrap up my talk. It usually works out that way when I have to lecture in English: I take too long and I end up scrambling to finish.

My talk was about ceramic proton conductors. I had placed these conductors in deuterium gas and, after repeated electrolysis, I observed excess heat and the production of new elements (See Appendix B.)

The audience was more interested in hearing about new element production (transmutation) than the excess heat. There were many questions about the ceramic material. Unfortunately, I myself still do not have the answers to many of these questions.

After all presentations were completed, an open discussion was held. Hal Fox (Fusion Information Center, Salt Lake City, Utah) and Tom Passell, (retired, EPRI - the Electric Power Research Institute, Palo Alto, California) contributed most to the discussion. As expected, the main focus was how to convince the wider scientific community to recognize the reality of cold fusion. Until it does, papers submitted to journals will be rejected, and grant applications will be turned down. The situation is the same in every country.

Even though our observations clearly indicate a real effect, we have to put up with censure from people who claim "experimental error," "contamination," and finally "lies and fraud." You can see how this field of research has become a tangled mess.

About Professor Bockris

Let me say a few things about Bockris. Bockris is a pillar of strength in the field of electrochemistry, but he himself used to be renowned for his reluctance to accept reports of new phenomena. When he debates with people, he starts by denying the point his opponent tries to make. It is said that in the 1970s he was close to getting the Nobel Prize, but his aggressive style alienated many people, who subsequently opposed the nomination.

During my postdoctoral research, Bockris and I could not agree how to interpret my data, so I ended up writing a paper which came to a completely unanticipated conclusion. The subject was pitting corrosion in iron, a form of corrosion triggered by chlorine. The issues were: Is the chlorine initially adsorbed onto the surface, or absorbed into the metal? When it is adsorbed or absorbed, how far down in the metal does it penetrate? In the end, our discussion broke down, we were unable to agree on anything.

Precisely because he is so stubborn, Bockris has continued to struggle on alone, without allies, continuing with cold fusion research, even though others refuse to believe it exists.

Although Bockris and I sometimes feuded while I worked on my postdoctorate, fundamentally I felt great respect for him. When he thinks he has solid results or a good argument, he does not flinch. He is the kind of person who goes for the truth; he does not ask, "What do most people say?" but instead he wants to know "Is it right?" In other words, "Is it scientifically correct or not?" This is not as simple—or as common—as you might think. In Japan, scientists tend to go with the flow, believing whatever the majority believes.

Periodic Table of the Elements

1 **H** Hydrogen 1.008																	2 **He** Helium 4.00
3 **Li** Lithium 6.94	4 **Be** Beryllium 9.01											5 **B** Boron 10.82	6 **C** Carbon 12.01	7 **N** Nitrogen 14.01	8 **O** Oxygen 16.00	9 **F** Fluorine 19.00	10 **Ne** Neon 20.17
11 **Na** Sodium 23.00	12 **Mg** Magnesium 24.32											13 **Al** Aluminum 26.98	14 **Si** Silicon 28.09	15 **P** Phosphorus 30.97	16 **S** Sulfur 32.06	17 **Cl** Chlorine 35.45	18 **Ar** Argon 39.95
19 **K** Potassium 39.10	20 **Ca** Calcium 40.08	21 **Sc** Scandium 44.96	22 **Ti** Titanium 47.90	23 **V** Vanadium 50.95	24 **Cr** Chromium 52.01	25 **Mn** Manganese 54.94	26 **Fe** Iron 55.85	27 **Co** Cobalt 58.94	28 **Ni** Nickel 58.71	29 **Cu** Copper 63.54	30 **Zn** Zinc 65.38	31 **Ga** Gallium 69.72	32 **Ge** Germanium 72.60	33 **As** Arsenic 74.91	34 **Se** Selenium 78.96	35 **Br** Bromine 79.90	36 **Kr** Krypton 83.80
37 **Rb** Rubidium 85.48	38 **Sr** Strontium 87.63	39 **Y** Yttrium 88.92	40 **Zr** Zirconium 91.22	41 **Nb** Niobium 92.91	42 **Mo** Molybdenum 95.95	43 **Tc** Technetium (99)	44 **Ru** Ruthenium 101.1	45 **Rh** Rhodium 102.91	46 **Pd** Palladium 106.4	47 **Ag** Silver 107.880	48 **Cd** Cadmium 112.41	49 **In** Indium 114.82	50 **Sn** Tin 118.70	51 **Sb** Antimony 121.87	52 **Te** Tellurium 127.61	53 **I** Iodine 126.91	54 **Xe** Xenon 131.30
55 **Cs** Cesium 132.91	56 **Ba** Barium 137.36	57 ***La** Lanthanum 138.92	72 **Hf** Hafnium 178.50	73 **Ta** Tantalum 180.95	74 **W** Tungsten 183.86	75 **Re** Rhenium 186.22	76 **Os** Osmium 190.2	77 **Ir** Iridium 192.2	78 **Pt** Platinum 195.05	79 **Au** Gold 197.0	80 **Hg** Mercury 200.61	81 **Tl** Thallium 204.39	82 **Pb** Lead 207.21	83 **Bi** Bismuth 209.00	84 **Po** Polonium (210)	85 **At** Astatine (210)	86 **Rn** Radon (222)
87 **Fr** Francium (223)	88 **Ra** Radium (226)	89 ****Ac** Actinium (227)	104 **Ku** Kurchatovium (261)	105 **Ha** Hahnium (260)													

Figure 2. Periodic Table of the Elements. Elements are ordered by atomic number. From left to right, top to bottom, the atoms grow heavier. Elements on the same column have similar chemical properties. White—non-metallic elements, dark gray—metallic elements, light gray—transition elements.

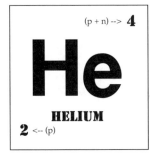

Figure 3. How to Read Element Symbols. Every element is represented by either a single capital letter or a capital and lowercase letter. Shown below is an example: helium. The atomic number indicates the number of protons (2), the mass number (4) indicates the total of protons (2) plus neutrons (2).

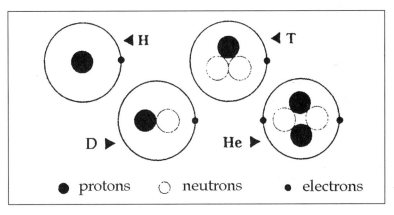

Figure 4. Hydrogen (H), deuterium (D), tritium (T), and helium (H). Hydrogen, deuterium and tritium have one proton and different numbers of neutrons. Helium atoms have two protons.

2

THE CURTAIN RISES ON COLD FUSION

An Old Neutron Generator

The Impact of the Fleischmann-Pons Announcement

On March 24, 1989, in the morning paper I saw a short article, only some ten lines long, tucked in the corner of a page. It was an extraordinary surprise. It said that electrochemists Martin Fleischmann (then 62 years old) of Southampton University, England, and Stanley Pons (then 48 years old) of the University of Utah in the U.S. announced at a press conference that they had produced "nuclear fusion during electrolysis."[1] According to the article, they used a palladium cathode in heavy water electrolyte, and observed copious excess heat production along with tritium and gamma rays from neutron collisions, which supported the hypothesis that this was fusion. From the article I inferred this was basically a simple liquid electrolysis experiment.

I was amazed to see this news. For one thing, I myself had been performing exactly the same kind of experiment for more than twenty years, but I had completely overlooked the reported phenomenon. It should be impossible to miss: if my cells had produced nuclear fusion they should have generated a large flux of radiation.

My Graduate Thesis

In 1967, my department at Hokkaido University was called Nuclear Engineering. Research topics here are common to other disciplines, so our positions are open to graduates from different departments. I transferred in as a first year graduate student from the Applied Physics Department. I entered the Reactor Materials Group. The theme I selected for my graduate thesis was "Absorption by Metals of Deuterons Implanted by an Ion Accelerator."

Both the Applied Physics and the Nuclear Engineering Departments had been recently established, so they were imbued with a cutting edge, up-and-coming spirit. You felt an eagerness to try things out, come what may.

Our new department in its new building inherited some old, abandoned equipment, including a neutron beam machine that was left lying around.

This is an accelerator that implants deuterons (the nuclei of heavy hydrogen atoms) into metal targets that have been saturated with deuterium or tritium, producing a stream of neutrons with a uniform power level (See Plate 1). I wondered whether this device could be used to study the behavior of deuterium implanted in metal.

The machine was installed in the four-mega-electron volt (4 MeV) linear accelerator room along with other equipment. The place resembled a half-underground shadowy, clammy concrete warehouse. The neutron beam machine had hardly been operated or even turned on for six years. When I tried to use it, I found it had vacuum chamber leaks, leaks from the high pressure plasma system, faults in the electronics, and a host of other problems. I finally got the neutron beam to work a year later, in January 1968. My graduate thesis was due in the middle of February. I managed to shoot heavy protons into a target of titanium saturated with deuterium, and I was able to read the neutron pulse from a BF_3 detector and an old-fashioned scintillation counter. (See the brief definitions of these technical terms in the glossary.)

It was the cold dead of winter, January in Hokkaido. Every evening and well into the night, long after the heating was turned off, I was down in the dark shadows by the bare concrete walls of the control room, operating the neutron generator. My goal was to saturate titanium with hydrogen.

Titanium is used in many common articles like golf clubs, eyeglass frames, and medical utensils. In some circumstances it begins rusting quickly and at the same time it absorbs large amounts of hydrogen. When titanium absorbs even a small amount of hydrogen, it becomes extremely brittle and it loses the strength needed to stand up to practical applications. This is called hydrogen embrittlement.

I took a sheet of titanium 0.3 millimeters thick and cut a disk 3 centimeters in diameter, which I placed in a solution of heavy water and heavy-hydrochloric acid (acid in which heavy hydrogen replaces regular hydrogen) for several days. The titanium began to corrode. The corrosion reaction freed up heavy hydrogen (deuterium), which was absorbed by the titanium to form deuterium compounds.

This natural form of corrosion was too slow, so I sped up the process by electrolyzing the solution, which forced more deuterium into the sample. This considerably shortened the time it took to perform the experiment. Later I employed this method exclusively. This process of loading the sample with deuterium by electrolysis is the same one that is used in cold fusion experiments.

After many setbacks I was finally able to load a large amount of heavy hydrogen into titanium. Near the surface, titanium hydride formed with loading close to a stoichiometric hydride, measured at D/Ti (the ratio of deuterium to titanium) of 1.97. I was finally able to complete my graduate thesis on March 13, 1968.

A Cell Produces Heat

Later, in addition to titanium targets, I electrolyzed zirconium, palladium, iron, nickel, and other metals in ordinary water and heavy water, and I irradiated them with the deuteron beam.

After finishing my doctorate and becoming an assistant professor, nearly every year I have advised students writing graduate theses or term papers on topics relating to hydrogen and metals. An especially memorable student was Takayuki Kurachi. Now a municipal employee, he came from Oshamanbe, a small town with a native Ainu name. He was a gangling, thin fellow, about 177 cm tall—an even-tempered student. He was extremely enthusiastic. He worked from morning until late at night every day, wrestling with the question of how zirconium absorbs hydrogen during electrolysis using various forms of water-based electrolytes. After electrolysis he measured hydrogen loading by dissolving the surface layers with a hydrogen fluoride solution and quantifying the volume of hydrogen released. He produced many interesting experimental results.

One such interesting result came in August 1978. At that time he was using a three-centimeter palladium disk electrolyzed in heavy water and D_2SO_4 (heavy sulphuric acid). The purpose was to create a target for the neutron generation machine, by saturating the metal with deuterium. He planned to leave the sample in electrolysis for about a week.

On the morning of the second day of electrolysis, Kurachi came to my office. "Dr. Mizuno, the electrolyte is gone," he said. "Did you remove it for analysis or something?"

"Huh?! What do you mean, 'gone'?" I responded.

"I mean that yesterday the cathode was entirely submerged in electrolyte, but when I got here this morning the waterline was below the cathode," he said.

I was shocked. I went to see for myself. The palladium certainly was sticking out of the water; the flow of electricity was completely cut off.

The cell held 200 cc of solution, and the power level had been 0.7 amperes, which is only enough to electrolyze about 6 cc of liquid per day. The 200 cc should have lasted a month.

The cell was a cylinder 6 cm in diameter, 15 centimeters tall. The solution was 7 cm deep. The anode and cathode were at the bottom, so in fifteen days there was no way the waterline should have fallen below the cathode. Furthermore, the top portion of the cell was more than sufficiently air cooled to prevent evaporation from joule heating.

We examined the cell closely but we found nothing out of the ordinary. There was no sign of physical damage, not so much as a tiny crack.

Hydrogen and oxygen effluent gases were separated in chambers within the cell, collected in a trap, and then expelled. This prevented recombination. That left only two possibilities: the electric current might have increased, rapidly electrolyzing all of the liquid, or a large amount of heat might have caused the fluid to boil away. But at the time we could not imagine either of those scenarios, so we finally wrote off the incident as a mystery with no solution. We did not understand it until many years later.

Gamma Rays Detected

It was May 1981. I was working with Dr. Mori from the Nuclear High Vacuum Research Department. (He is now with NASDA - the National Space Development Agency). We were loading titanium with deuterium.

We placed a 5 cm by 10 cm titanium foil in D_2O - D_2SO_4 (heavy water and heavy sulfuric acid), and began three days of electrolysis. By the end of the first day the surface was nearly saturated, forming a layer TiD_2 (titanium deuteride).

That evening we activated an X-ray detector adjacent to the cell. It suddenly began to register continuous bursts of X-rays. In a panic, we checked our clothes and belongings for radioactive contamination. We moved the detector around to find the source of the X-rays. We finally concluded that the cell must be the source. But at the time we never imagined electrolysis could produce X-rays, so after careful consideration we decided it must be some kind of electrical interference. It turned out the cell really was generating X-rays, but I did not realize that until much later.

Later, after I learned to operate the linear accelerator to produce a type of nuclear fusion in metal targets, it occurred to me that some similar form of low level nuclear fusion might be occurring in the electrolysis cell. I had in mind a model of the kind that was popular in the early days of cold fusion research: the deuterons in the metal hydride might be crowded together more than they are in liquids or other solids, to the point where in some cases deuteron fusion might be triggered by an external stimulus. This kind of hypothesis would occur to any researcher studying metal and hydrogen systems. It is not a particularly profound or outstanding idea. I never thought to pursue the matter and research the phenomenon further.

A Cold Fusion Replication

Preparations for an Experiment

Because of my extensive experience with electrolytic systems, the news of cold fusion made a big impact on me. March 25, the day after I heard the news, was a Saturday. I thought I would start a replication experiment that very day.

First, I got out an old partially-closed cell and I washed it many times with distilled water. Then I prepared the heavy water solution.

I had five 100-gram ampules of heavy water, and about 10 grams of pure lithium. Lithium looks a bit like hardened bean paste. The outside layers were gray with oxidation. Inside, it had a bright metallic luster. I used a utility knife to cut away the contaminated outside layers, leaving 0.7 grams, a block about one centimeter on each side, like a sugar cube. I dropped it into the cell which contained 200 cc of heavy water. In contrast to sodium, lithium dissolves quietly, without exploding or splattering. In five or six minutes the solution was ready.

Next, I prepared the electrodes. I had several platinum samples in hand, so I soon had an anode ready. The palladium cathode was the problem. I had obtained a fax copy of the Fleischmann-Pons paper, but it did not describe any details about the materials or the electrolyte. I had no idea what the proper configuration should be, or the purity of the materials, or what material treatments to perform.

Based on my experience, I concluded that the main goal should be to load as much deuterium into the metal as possible. I prepared a cathode made of a palladium tube that had been closed at one end. It was 3 mm in diameter and 10 cm long. I used a 2-amp, 30-volt power supply that happened to be lying around.

I assumed a nuclear reaction would have to give off radiation, so I put a simple Geiger counter near the cell to measure gamma radiation. If massive heat was going to be produced, it should be simple enough to measure, so I passed a thin, K-type thermocouple sheathed in Teflon through one of the holes in the cell lid, sealed the hole with silicon rubber, and set the thermocouple near the palladium rod.

To measure whether the cell is producing excess heat, it is necessary to determine the cell constant before the experiment begins. In other words, you must calibrate to determine how high the temperature will rise for a given level of input power. For that purpose I prepared another palladium cathode and electrolyte made from ordinary light water.

After completing preparations, I commenced electrolysis that afternoon. At first, no deuterium bubbles appeared on the palladium, even though oxygen bubbles were vigorously produced on the anode. This was a good sign: the deuterium was being absorbed by the cathode without a hitch.

At this stage, electrolysis current density was set for 10 milliamperes per square centimeter. About 100 milliamperes of current were supplied at 5 volts, so total power consumption was 0.5 watts. The anode and cathode were separated by a glass filter to prevent commingling of the materials by galvanic deposition.

After ten minutes of electrolysis, small bubbles gradually began appearing on the cathode surface. As time passed the bubbling became more intense. At this point the meter attached to the thermocouple registered 0.12 millivolts, indicating a temperature rise of three degrees. The cell constant was 7 degrees per watt, so I knew the input power was closely balanced with output heat.

Also, the gamma detector—the most important thing—was nominal, indicating nothing unusual. The needle vibrated from time to time as it registered the normal background. Clearly, nothing interesting was happening.

Measuring Neutrons

It was March 29, five days later. I was talking about the experiment with Assistant Professor Tadashi Akimoto of the Nuclear Reactor Engineering Department. He has twenty years experience in neutron measurement, and is superbly qualified to assess neutron detection techniques and data analysis. Akimoto and I have been friends since I was an undergraduate. He was in the class three years ahead of me. He worked his way through college, graduating from Hokkaido's Electrical Engineering Department. He joined the newly-established Nuclear Engineering Department and concentrated on teaching and research. His specialty is neutron detection. He is credited with many contributions to the field of nuclear reactor neutron spectral analysis, low energy neutron detection, and development of neutron detection systems. He is a talented and cooperative researcher.

In my discussions with Akimoto we agreed that if some form of nuclear reaction occurs, it obviously must generate neutrons, and we should be able to determine the nature of the reaction by measuring the energy spectrum. For example, a D-D (deuteron - deuteron) nuclear fusion reaction will produce a single 2.45 mega-electron-volt (MeV) peak. With a D-T (deuteron - tritium) reaction, you should see a 14 MeV peak.

Measuring a neutron spectrum is not easy. Measuring the energy of an X-ray, a gamma ray or a charged particle is comparatively straightforward. But, as you can tell from the name, a "neutron" is an electrically neutral particle that does not directly trigger an electromagnetic detector. You must use an indirect, highly specialized method to detect a neutron.

Because they are electrically neutral, neutrons readily pass through matter, but the kinetic energy of the neutron can affect matter, and vice versa. When a neutron strikes a hydrogen atom, the lightest of all atoms, the neutron loses much of its energy. Neutrons and hydrogen atoms have the same mass, so the neutron simply transfers most of its momentum to the hydrogen atom.

You can see an example of momentum transfer by putting two coins on a table. Flick one directly into the other. The first one stops; the one that was hit moves away. A neutron detector works on the same principle. Try this and you will soon note that "hitting" can be complicated. The moving coin might strike the edge of the stationary one, making both coins move away at different angles. The energy lost from the moving body will vary depending on the angle.

Based on this principle, you can analyze the energy from the collisions. You make a neutron detector with a substance containing a lot of hydrogen. When electrically charged hydrogen nuclei are struck by neutrons, they move and they cause another substance in the mixture to emit light. The strength of the light generated by the other substance indirectly indicates the energy of the neutrons. This instrument for measuring the neutron energy spectrum is called a liquid scintillation detector.

This is a simplified explanation. To be more exact, you establish sensitivity and calibrate the instrument at various known neutron energy levels. The most difficult task is to isolate the machine from sources of noise. After many complex procedures and much work, you finally establish the neutron energy.

When there are few neutrons, to get a reliable spectrum you must leave the detector and the experimental process in a steady state for weeks, to gradually build up data. Keeping the machine in a stable condition during that time can be a terrific nuisance. Another problem is that the environment is constantly bombarded with neutrons from outer space and from radioactive materials in the ground, and these "background" neutrons interfere with the measurements and cloak the neutrons you are looking for.

The energy from these background neutrons covers a wide range, and it varies from place to place and at different times of day. Approximately 100 of these neutrons pass through our bodies every ten seconds, occasionally colliding with something and causing a reaction. For these reasons, measuring neutrons is a tough job that requires considerable experience and carefully selected instruments.

Soon after I talked with Akimoto, we built a neutron detection system in his laboratory. We used the meters and the energy spectrum detector he had on hand. Directly in front of the meter, on a small adjustable platform, we placed the electrolysis cell. To keep neutrons on the outside from getting in, we surrounded the cell and detector with a wall about 30 centimeters thick, made up of white blocks of paraffin wax containing boron.

Boron readily absorbs neutrons, so it is often used as a "moderator" to slow or stop them. It is mixed in with paraffin or plastic, both of which contain a lot of hydrogen. Cadmium is also used as a moderator. Materials like this can have a big effect on the neutron energy.

From outside, the detector looked like a small, white, squared-off Eskimo igloo. With this, on the morning of March 31, 1989, we launched our experiment to analyze the neutron energy spectrum. We were looking for decisive evidence of a nuclear reaction.

Up until this time the electrolysis current density had been about 10 milliamps per square centimeter. But, since no new results appeared I increased the current five times over, up to 50 milliamps per square centimeter. That meant the total current was 0.5 amperes. In tandem with this, voltage increased to 20 volts.

Input was 10 watts. Most of this energy was consumed heating up the glass filter between the anode and cathode. The temperature sensor output increased to 3 millivolts, indicating that the temperature had risen to 75°C. The cell was too hot to touch with bare hands. This was obviously not heat from the so-called cold fusion reaction.

We continued at this level of electrolysis for three days. We did not obtain any particularly significant neutron spectrum signature. With or without interesting results, electrolysis consumed five grams of heavy water every day, and it had to be replenished every three days or the top of the palladium cathode would soon have been sticking out of the water.

The situation remained unchanged, so I increased current density up to 100 milliamps per square centimeter, and I decided to electrolyze only the bottom half of the palladium. By doing this, I was able to increase total amperage to 500 milliamps, doubling current density. Even under these electrolysis conditions there was no significant neutron signature or excess heat.

If a D-D reaction was occurring, it should have produced neutrons, helium and protons, as well as tritium and gamma rays. So we were looking for such products. To look for tritium, we analyzed samples of the electrolyte with a liquid scintillator at the Radioisotope Center on campus, but the tritium concentration did not appear to be any different from samples taken before electrolysis began. We did not see any increases above the error limits of the detector.

We Decide to Try Again

It was April 7, a week after we began this experimental run. I consulted with Akimoto again. There were no positive results confirming neutrons, gamma rays, tritium, excess heat, or any other definitive proof of a nuclear reaction. For my part, without a positive incentive to continue, I did not think I could justify doing the experiment. Akimoto was more wary of reaching any conclusion.

He believed we had not experimented sufficiently long enough to decide anything yet. He emphasized that we could not reach a conclusion yet because we had no idea what the experiment required in four areas:

1. Material conditions, material preparation, morphology, contaminants, surface conditions.

2. Electrochemical conditions: current density, temperature, electrolyte.

3. The expected conditions for detecting neutrons.

4. The conditions for detecting other nuclear products and effects like protons, helium, or X-rays.

He pointed out that no research team had yet reported any sign of neutrons, so if the reaction did produce neutrons, it was not producing many, and any reaction that was occurring must be very small. In which case, we would almost certainly not see neutrons because our laboratory background was so noisy. Any neutrons from our experiment would be lost in the noise. In the end we decided to move the experimental apparatus to a location with better background conditions, and try again.

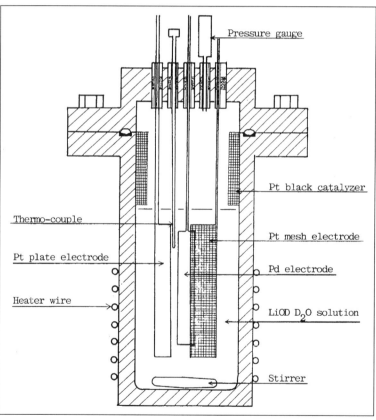

Figure 5. Cross section of Mizuno's closed cell.

3

THE FIRST REPLICATION

Measuring Neutrons in the Underground Laboratory

The Hokkaido University Nuclear Engineering Department has several accelerators which, when operated, produce powerful radiation. Obviously this radiation cannot be allowed to harm the environment, so the accelerators are surrounded by extremely tough shielding. They are usually placed in underground laboratories: chambers with thick walls of reinforced concrete, covered over by a deep layer of earth, from which virtually no radiation leaks into the surroundings. By the same token, almost no stray natural radiation from the surroundings can leak into these facilities. An experiment must be set up in a place like this to avoid noise and to improve the sensitivity and precision of the apparatus.

Fortunately, the underground facilities housing the 4-mega-electron-volt linear accelerator are extensive. Some of the rooms in the facility have hardly been opened for years.

A small building above ground leads to the underground complex. It is among the engineering experimental lab buildings, which are built alongside the famous picturesque row of poplar trees. Just beyond the building are the barns and fields of the Agriculture Department experimental farm. Behind a wire fence next to the laboratory, chickens run around and horses and donkeys placidly munch grass. It is a tranquil country landscape.

Although the building was constructed only fifteen years ago, the outside walls are already patched where they have cracked. It is anything but pretty.

To get to the underground lab from my office, you go down an outside staircase at the back of my building, and past a chain-link fence. About 100 meters down the road are the grounds of the linear accelerator. You pass four large poplar trees along the driveway to the entrance building.

Inside the building is an electronic checkpoint. You sign in, run a magnetic strip card through a reader, and a door opens automatically. You go another 20 meters to the top of a flight of stairs leading down into the underground laboratories. You go down five meters, another automatic door opens, and the control room comes into view.

You walk through the control room, past the banks of meters and instruments, and off to one side you find another door. This is a massive, electrically-driven barrier on rails, four meters thick, four meters wide, two meters tall. When it opens, there before your eyes is the large tube that makes up the heart of the linear accelerator. This tube is mounted only 120 centimeters off the floor. You have to duck down to walk underneath it, then you walk alongside the tube farther back into the lab, and finally you approach your goal. Over the door is a sign "Neutron Time-of-Flight Detection Lab."

Another massive one-meter thick electrically-operated door guards this lab. You press the button and it slowly opens with a rumbling noise. Inside is a labyrinth of small chambers filled with equipment. In the farthest one back, there in the gloomy half-light, we constructed the cold fusion neutron detection experiment.

The place has a massive roof made of heavy concrete a meter thick, which is covered by five meters of earth. There is a two tier floor, also made of reinforced heavy concrete. In the recessed lower tier of the floor is a pool of water about 50 centimeters deep. Water is the best protection against the penetration of radiation from below. Akimoto spent three days constructing the neutron detection system in this place.

The equipment was mounted on a heavy table 1 meter tall, 1.6 meters wide, 2 meters long, inside a structure built with a few dozen white plastic blocks that looked like bricks: a neutron moderator. Around the outside of this wall was another layer of moderator blocks made of paraffin filled with boron. Together the two layers effectively screened out nearly all neutrons.

In the center of the structure was the neutron energy detector, an Ne-213 scintillator. This is a cylinder about 20 centimeters in diameter, and 20 centimeters long. Next to it was an optical fiber attached to a photomultiplier that amplified the signal from the scintillator hundreds of millions of times. Several cables linked the equipment to the high voltage power supply, the pre-amp power supply, and the signal counter.

After you set up this complicated and troublesome nest of equipment you are finally ready to begin measuring the neutron energy spectrum. The principle is simple enough. As I explained earlier, neutrons collide and bounce like coins or other macroscopic bodies. (See Chapter 2, "Measuring Neutrons.") When a neutron flies into the scintillator and collides with a proton in the liquid, it transfers some portion of its energy to the proton. This makes the proton move. Protons, unlike neutrons, carry an electrical charge, and they form strong electron bonds with fluorescent substances. The movement of the protons excites electrons in the outer shells of the other material, which emits light. You study neutrons indirectly by measuring the light. The number of light flashes (photons) corresponds to the energy of the neutrons, allowing you to determine the spectrum of the energy. If the neutrons come from D-D fusion reactions, they carry 2.45 MeV of energy, and you find a bulge or peak in the spectrum curve in the corresponding spot. When many neutrons are generated it is easy to distinguish this peak, but when there are only a few neutrons it is terribly difficult, and takes a long time. As I said previously, neutrons pass through matter easily. It is hard to shield against them. In the underground lab background neutrons were reduced to a hundredth of the above-ground rate, but it would have been nice to reduce them even more, virtually to zero. During long term measurements, the detector registered neutrons of various energy levels. Over the whole spectrum, the number of low energy neutrons is exponentially larger than high energy ones. This is because in most cases the energy from a neutron is not completely transferred in a direct head on collision, but instead it is only partially transferred by a glancing blow.

Chaos

By this time the whole world was in an uproar about cold fusion. Professor Oyama of Tokyo A&M University had announced during a conference that he had observed tritium and gamma rays. It turned out he got carried away. He was overreaching, he was later unable to replicate these results. This sort of thing was happening all over the world, in mass chaos.

The chaos spread to Hokkaido University. The department head at this time was Professor Norio Sato, whose field of expertise was electrochemistry, so he welcomed the concept of cold fusion. He gathered a group of experts on the staff to inaugurate a Hokkaido University Cold Fusion Research Team. But actually, I was the only person actually doing any research in this field, so the "team" functioned mainly as a forum for me to present my results, and in which to compare my results with reports from other workers filtering in from all over the world. At the second meeting of this team, I presented my results up to that point for neutrons, gamma rays, and excess heat, which had all been completely negative. As I explained, I had done only one run, the equipment was not fully prepared yet, and the system was still crude. You might say this was a trial run. But, as it happened, the data I presented was later used behind my back in a tiresome fashion. Professor B, close to retirement, and Professor A called a press conference, something we never considered doing. These two professors had analyzed the data from Fleischmann and Pons and they announced at the press conference they had found errors in the formulas and defects in the data in the paper, which they combined with the data from my trial run to reach the conclusion that cold fusion does not exist.

When I came to the classroom that day, I found the place was in an uproar with reporters and television station film crews swarming around. In the middle of the crowd Professor A was holding forth, telling the reporters that in his opinion "cold fusion has no scientific basis." He was handing out copies of my data. At the previous meeting our research team had concluded that there was no clear evidence that cold fusion had occurred, and that we should continue the experiment for a little while longer. We decided to leave the decision on whether to continue the experiment to the Dean of Engineering, Professor Sato. He had left the country on a trip in early April, and had planned to judge the results when he returned. Professor A took it upon himself to call a press conference on the morning of April 21, a Friday.

At that point, without sufficient data, after having studied only one paper on the subject, why did Professor A rush to categorically reject cold fusion? There may be many reasons, but I think that one is related to the energy crisis. While Hokkaido University is a member of the nuclear energy research establishment, it is only a provincial university and its professors have little influence compared with government administrators or power company officials. It does not contribute much impetus to the development of nuclear energy. From the start, cold fusion was promoted as a limitless and clean source of concentrated heat. It was just what the anti-nuclear movement was looking for. Furthermore, the nuclear research camp was already divided into advocates of fission and fusion. Add to that Professor Sato's reputation for leadership in breaking new ground, and you have a potent brew of politics and infighting. Professor A was trying to improve his standing within the establishment by attacking the newcomers. This sort of thing can happen anywhere; it is not unusual in scientific research.

But it is important to ask if this is the attitude a researcher ought to take. Is it ethical? Scientific truth becomes clear after you examine much data, and many hypotheses. Based upon these hypotheses you perform experiments, and you repeat them many times before reaching a conclusion. No matter how absurd a report of something new may sound, no matter how unscientific, you can only begin to judge where it is headed after much research and many experiments. Sometimes it takes a considerable amount of time and effort before the situation becomes clear. History shows that in many cases a report of a novel phenomenon turns out to be a mistake, or even, occasionally, a lie. Examples are described in other books, so I will not go into them here. My point is that science has progressed to the present day largely by trial and error.

One thing this progress has taught us is the importance of replicability. But this issue is widely misunderstood. Ideally, anyone, anywhere should be able to achieve the same results. Before others can replicate your work, you are supposed to precisely define all experimental conditions. That is the ideal, but real science often does not work that way. In most materials science experiments, there are too many experimental conditions to be precisely defined. When a reaction occurs on the surface or in the interface between materials it can be even more complicated, giving researchers a devil of a time. Even commercial material science processes often depend upon poorly defined, hit-or-miss recipes.

When a system can be divided into a small set of constituent components, a phenomenon may be easy to comprehend. But when a system is built up of many interacting components in a large, complex entity, the system and its components can be extraordinarily difficult to analyze. Weather forecasting, predicting earthquakes or economic trends, the study of living bodies in biology, and today's trendy chaos theories all attempt to shed light on complex systems—with great difficulty, as everyone knows. There are many similar examples proving that it simply is not true that a phenomenon has no scientific basis just because it cannot be replicated at will or analyzed according to first principles.

Support from the Department Head

The April 21 press conference surprised not only our research team, but the other researchers within the university. Naturally, I was shocked by these developments. Although it was called a "research team" the only "members" were me, myself and I, and later Akimoto. The other participants were not performing experiments, so the call to discontinue "replication experiments" boiled down to the demand that Akimoto and I abandon our work. From the start it was clear that cold fusion fell into my bailiwick. It involved the behavior of hydrogen in metals. It called for almost exactly the same kinds of experiments I had been performing for years, so I was eager to proceed. A scientist's attitude is critical to the success or failure of a research project. The researcher must be sincerely interested and enthusiastic. Enthusiasm is what makes him willing to throw himself into the work wholeheartedly. The key to good university research is to find the right topic and then concentrate on it. The university's job is to ensure an environment in which scientists can concentrate on their work, and ultimately return the benefits of their research to society.

When Sato returned from overseas after the negativist press conference, and he learned about the newspapers, television reports and so on, he hurriedly called me in and asked me the details of the matter. When he learned what had happened, Sato was surprised and disappointed. He was particularly let down by the bad attitudes toward research, the lack of spirit. Sato himself is a noted electrochemist. He has a deep-rooted friendship with

Fleischmann and Pons, and he knew that when two researchers of this caliber make an important announcement, something must be up. He thought it was essential that we perform sufficient replication experiments ourselves before reaching any conclusion. When I met with Sato, I reported that the experiment was still underway, that Akimoto had joined in the effort, and that we had moved the cell to a more suitable environment. I emphasized in particular that a definitive result in this experiment would be the detection of neutrons, which would be nuclear reaction products. As a result, Sato allocated special internal funding for our project. Later, with this extra money, we were able to modernize our neutron detector and achieve important results.

Detecting Neutrons

After we began electrolysis Akimoto checked the neutron detector regularly four times every day at 8 a.m., 12 p.m., 4 p.m., and 8 p.m., squeezing in the work between his regular research and teaching assignments. He did not take a single day off for holidays or weekends. He checked the neutron readings, the calibration, and the computer. I checked the system at 9:00 every morning, observing the temperature, electric power, water level, cathode, and so on. We continued with the experiment, even though we had only a slight expectation that anything would come of it.

It was the morning of May 15, about one month after we had initiated electrolysis. Moments after I arrived to teach my regular Monday morning class, Akimoto called me on the telephone. "Get over here, would you? We have a peak in the spectrum," he said in a curiously loud voice. He is usually such a cool-headed individual, I ran to the underground lab, wondering what could have gotten into him.

There was Akimoto, beckoning to me from the back of the gloomy, half-lit, narrow concrete-walled room, wearing a grubby white laboratory coat and a perplexed expression. The neutron energy spectrum data was displayed on a screen, after complex computer processing. This information, known as "unfolding data," was still in what you might call a "raw" form that must be further processed to bring out the peak. The trace line was shaped like a gentle downward slope, but towards the bottom there was a bulge, like a miniature ski jump. "What is this?" I asked. Akimoto answered slowly, "I think it may be a peak caused by 2.45 MeV neutrons . . ."

"Meaning what? Could this neutron energy level come from a D-D fusion reaction?"

"That's right. Have another look at the spectrum," said Akimoto, as he turned the knob to display different memory blocks in the multi-channel analyzer.

The distribution of points in this data set was different. It traced a gradually declining line with no ski jump bulge in the middle. According to Akimoto, this was the background measured when the detector was held 5 meters away from the cell. In this case the 2.45 MeV neutrons were not detected. This was done twice, and in both cases the peak was only seen when the detector was placed near the cell.

I said, "That means the electrolysis is creating some phenomenon that produces the 2.45 MeV peak, or you might say, D-D fusion. Isn't that what it means?"

"You might say that. But I have only done the experiment twice. I have to try it many more times under varying conditions. It is too soon to reach a conclusion. It's possible we picked up some random noise or something."

"Random noise? What do you mean by that?" I asked. I was not sure how a neutron detector could pick up noise. In the measurements I had done over the years, I used an accelerator which produces a giant flux of neutrons, orders of magnitude greater than the one we were dealing with now, so I had no experience with the noise problems we faced. When I performed experiments with a D-D reaction, I used a cylindrical BF_3 detector, and I counted 10^5 to 10^7 neutrons per second. Noise was simply not an issue. But with cold fusion we had to look for a neutron spectrum formed by 10^{-2} or 10^{-3} neutrons per second. To derive a meaningful spectrum we had to accumulate data for 10^6 seconds (12 ~ 13 days) continuously. We had to keep the detector stable this entire time. Expert though he was, Akimoto had never tried to measure such a weak flux of neutrons. Every day he checked several times to make sure the detector was still stable, and still working correctly.

Akimoto explained: "Listen, Mizuno, you may not realize it, but neutron detectors count a lot of other things besides neutrons. All kinds of stuff shows up on the Ne-213. Neutrons of course, but also X-rays, gamma rays, cosmic rays, electromagnetic waves . . . and they are affected by changes in light, temperature and humidity. When you have a large neutron flux it is no big deal. But with so few neutrons you have to keep the detector stable over many days, which is no easy trick. You have to filter out the noise. That, by George, calls for a real pro. It is especially difficult to separate gamma rays and neutrons. You tell them apart by looking at the shape of the pulse, and then you draw a line between the gamma and neutron signals, which is a real pain. You have to calibrate over and over with a neutron source. I check that segment of the spectrum every day."

What Akimoto called the "shape of the pulse" refers primarily to the rise time. A gamma ray makes a sharp and quick pulse whereas a neutron makes a slow, wide pulse—up to an order of magnitude slower. We calibrated with a 50 micro Curie Cf-252 neutron source.

"Well, it sounds like you can draw the line anywhere you like, and make the peak appear one day and disappear the next. How do you know it is exactly 2.45 MeV? It could be a coincidence. Why does the peak appear when the cell is present?" I asked, raising my voice.

"That's what I don't know yet. There might be any number of explanations. The gamma-n separation may be off, or something else may be at fault," Akimoto answered, also raising his voice.

"Okay. Your point is that we can't tell without taking more data. In that case, we should beef up the reaction. Power density is now 100 mA, so I'll try doubling it. The anode glass filter looks like it's in bad shape, so I'll switch over to the other anode."

This cell was constructed with two compartments on either side with anodes in them. When you used both anodes, you could increase amperage without raising voltage much. Most of the electric power was expended at the filter. However, heavy water consumption was proportional to power expended, and with this cell it was becoming lavish, with as much as 10 grams of electrolyte evaporated every day. As always, the power was 100 watts, pushing the temperature up to 80°C, which made the cell too hot to touch with a bare hand. Akimoto worried about the effect of this temperature on his instruments, and the effects of the electrolysis power supply, but afterward we tested and verified that neither of these factors has a measurable effect on the energy spectrum.

I decided to increase electrolysis power beginning that day. Akimoto continued collecting data onto tape and analyzing it. At that point we were using 100 gram glass ampules of 99.75% pure heavy water. We were paying 14,000 yen each, and we used them up at the rate of one every ten days, so there was no way we could afford to keep the experiment going much longer. (We later arranged volume discounts which brought the price down to 10,000 yen, which is still a lot of money.)

What to do? Somehow it seemed to me the critical factor was not deuterium loading after all. I pondered the problem, and thought to myself: ordinarily to accelerate a reaction, you increase temperature or pressure. To try that I'll need to make a reaction vessel I can pressurize. I guess it would be best to produce the hydrogen and oxygen within a single chamber, and convert them back into water with a catalytic recombiner. As the deuterium goes into the palladium, oxygen will be left behind. Could it be dangerous? Might it explode? No, that can be effectively prevented, and the free gas has some advantages: the volume of oxygen left behind indicates how much deuterium is in the palladium. And you do not have to worry as much about contamination. That was my train of thought . . . and in no time I got to work designing a closed cell.

Ten days passed. It was the morning of May 5 when I went to Akimoto's lab. He handed me the papers he was working on and asked, "What do you think of this?" It had two spectrograms (see Figure 6; 7a,b). The first sheet clearly showed a strong 2.5 MeV peak. On the second there was no peak at all.

"This is very clear, isn't it? 2.5 MeV means we are looking at neutrons from a D-D reaction, right? This is 2.45 MeV, within a reasonable range of error. For the time being I can think of no reason to doubt we have a cold fusion reaction."

"How many times have you measured it?" I asked faintly. My heart skipped a beat.

"Three times. In all three this 2.45 MeV peak comes out only with electrolysis. In the background you see nothing," said Akimoto, cool-headed to the last.

"Well, in that case, why don't we report this immediately, and submit a paper. Of course we aren't the first in the world. I guess this is fairly close to the results from Jones *et al.* at Brigham Young University. They say they have not observed any sign of excess heat, but they do report neutrons. Only, maybe it would be better to wait on the paper until we have a chance to look for tritium. Okay, here is the most important clue to the structure of the reaction: let's try to figure it based on the neutron production rate. Generally speaking, over twenty days we see about 10^6 neutrons, and this should yield about 1 joule of heat energy, which we could not possibly detect. Tritium is also difficult to detect, they say. Of course this is all predicated on the idea that the reaction is D-D fusion . . ." I pressed on, nonstop.

Akimoto interrupted. He spoke slowly, in a soothing manner. "Wait a second. Don't get ahead of yourself. I am an expert in measurement techniques, and I need to change the conditions and measure again, many more times. I do not want to rush to present a conclusion. Some aspects of this make me uneasy. You may not know it, but as I told you before various factors can have a subtle effect on the peak. To start with, the cell is hot, isn't it? That might have an effect. The thing is, there are not enough neutrons for me to feel comfortable. We are talking about numbers ten and even twenty orders of magnitude below the levels I am used to dealing with. We have no idea what could be influencing the instruments. Furthermore, a tentative report of negative cold fusion results has already been issued in the name of the Hokkaido University study group. Issued by two of your superiors, I might add. What do you think will happen to an assistant professor such as yourself, if you publish another report that overturns their conclusions? Don't misunderstand me. I'll support you all the way. But I'm saying you must be cautious."

His words made me think twice. I suggested it would be best to talk it over with Professor Sato. "Okay, I understand," I said. "Here's what we'll do. Let us stay with the problem: keep verifying as much as you like. But I'll report your tentative results to the head of the engineering department. I think he'll be delighted." I gave careful consideration to the idea of publishing. Then, on the afternoon of that day, I contacted Department Head Sato, and reported on the continuing progress of the experiment.

I showed Sato the spectrograms. His voice grew shrill with excitement. "This is amazing. It's incredibly distinct, isn't it? Now I understand what has

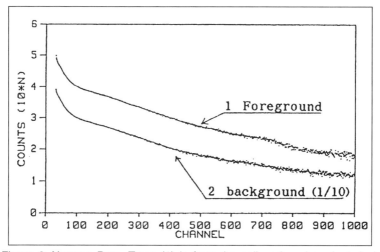

Figure 6. Neutron Data. Trace (1) is from the cell undergoing electrolysis. From channel 700 to 800 a gentle peak is seen. This corresponds to 2.45 MeV of energy. (2) is without electrolysis. Clearly, no peak is seen. Both of these traces represent "unfolding data" which is accumulated over a period of weeks. The data has not yet been processed to show the spectrum.

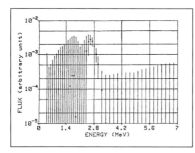
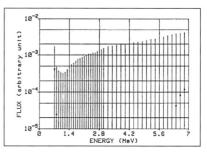

Figure 7a, 7b. Data taken from the previous graph (Fig. 6), and converted into a spectrum by computer processing. (a) during electrolysis, (b) when electrolysis is stopped, with the background subtracted. In the electrolysis spectrum, a peak is apparent at 2.5 MeV, but when electrolysis is stopped this peak does not appear.

got into you. As researchers, our job has significance when we pull our results together in a paper and show the world what we have accomplished. Okay, prepare your results right away. I'll meet with Akimoto and ask him to brief me directly on these graphs. Then the three of us will discuss this." He was excited. "Let's hold another urgent staff research symposium where you can report these results," he continued.

For my part, I was not inclined to report at a staff symposium. It had already been reported within the university that the project had been axed, and a rumor was going around that the research group had broken up. I did not feel like issuing a contradictory report. I spoke frankly to Sato.

He responded, "That isn't the case at all. It is clear from Professor A's press conference that he was critiquing the paper by Fleischmann and Pons. He made no reference to the results from Jones. Our final policy is supposed to be decided in consultation with me. Furthermore . . . what passes for science is not cast in concrete. It progresses day by day; what passes for common sense yesterday can change overnight, as you well know. The important question is, are you conducting your research logically and scientifically?"

When I heard this I could think of nothing to say in response. I said I understood, but I added: "I'd like to get Akimoto's okay on the final version of the paper. For my part, I would like to present this work as soon as possible."

"I understand. I'll speak with Akimoto myself, soon," said Sato.

The Report on Neutron Detection

The Cold Fusion Discussion Group met under the direction of Engineering Department Head Sato on the first floor of the south wing of the Hokkaido University Engineering Department Main Building. Some 35 people participated, and the main topic of discussion was my report on the neutron detection results. I addressed the meeting for twenty minutes. I described how we had moved the apparatus to the underground laboratory, and increased the power density, temperature, and the planned duration of the experiment. We were performing neutron detection as rigorously as we knew how to. We detected sporadic yet continuing neutrons at a level 10 ~ 20 times greater than background; and the energy levels were close to 2.45 MeV, the expected level for D-D fusion. Keeping the discussion calm and objective, I explained that we were not doing extensive calorimetry, and we saw no change in tritium levels comparing before and after samples. Based on the neutrons, our conclusion was that some sort of nuclear reaction was probably occurring. I reported furthermore that we were in the process of submitting a paper on these results to an electrochemical journal, with three authors listed, including Sato.

We wrote this paper from May 26 to the 28, finishing up the last touches in the second floor study of Sato's house. Sato and I lived in the same housing complex so it was easy for us to stay in contact. I wrote up the whole draft in a three-day stretch, meeting with him after supper to debate the finer points. The contents of the paper we submitted were exactly the same as the presentation I gave at the discussion group. The paper was accepted in two weeks. Referee comments, corrections and the like were exchanged by fax. It was published with exceptional speed.[2] Incidentally, a reporter by the name Nagayama from the *Hokkaido Shimbun* newspaper attended the discussion group, with permission from the department head. When he heard what I had to say he could not hide his excitement. Nagayama was only twenty-nine at the time. He had deep knowledge of science, since he graduated from the Hokkaido University department of synthetic chemistry before becoming a reporter.

He and I had previous contact when we discussed research in metal hydrides. He introduced my work to the public in an article in the *Hokkaido Shimbun* newspaper monthly magazine. He was aware that I was doing cold fusion research from the time of the Fleischmann-Pons announcement, when he had contacted me for comments. Sato told him about the university engineering department research group. My report was the first confirmation of cold fusion in the nation, so it was big news for Nagayama. With the consent of the department head, he quickly wrote an article.

On June 3 a five-column article appeared on the front page of the *Hokkaido Shimbun*. "A Successful Replication of Cold Fusion—First in the Nation, Neutrons are Detected" was the rather sensational headline. The article was accurate, focusing only on neutrons. But the term "successful replication" was an overstatement. I was afraid people would take this to mean we had recreated the Fleischmann-Pons experiment in its entirety. This had never been our original intention. The article carried Nagayama's byline, which is rare in Japan, where most news articles are anonymous. This was his way of showing us his sense of commitment to the story. For me, the article marked the beginning of deep involvement with cold fusion.

About the First Conferences and Meetings

After we reported neutrons, some of the mass media coverage was amazing. I was swamped with inquiries for the next two years.

I was contacted by television networks, newspapers and magazines not only in Japan but from overseas, one after another. It got to be too much for me. I was overwhelmed. I received invitation after invitation to lecture at institutes and conferences. It interfered with my research.

Let me describe some of the early cold fusion conferences that left a strong impression in my mind.

The first formal conference at which cold fusion results were presented began at 10:00 a.m. on Monday, July 31, 1989, under the auspices of the Electrochemical Society in the Tokyo Keidanren Hall. That Society, along with the Japan Nuclear Energy Society, are presently among the few that allow presentations on the subject of cold fusion.

The first members to participate included Hiroo Numata of the Tokyo Institute of Technology, Akito Takahashi of Osaka University, Department of Nuclear Engineering, and Ken'ichiro Ota of Yokohama National University, who are among the few researchers still promoting and making significant contributions to the field. They treat this as just another part of science, like any other topic they have researched in the past. They have pursued the research without flagging against the headwinds of adversity. They have performed scientific, empirical experiments resulting in important findings. This conference was the first opportunity in Japan for researchers to present cold fusion results, making it an epochal event in a sense. The presentations themselves were not sensational. They were mainly devoted to reaction products like heat and gamma rays from palladium in heavy water electrolysis, and to the metallurgy of hydrogen and palladium reactions. The papers were modest and conservative. I think the great value of this meeting was that it toned down the sensationalism, and helped make cold fusion a normal scientific field. Takahashi's paper, which dealt with the effect of changes in current density, was particularly valuable. It has had a long term effect on the field. Other significant papers clarified neutron measurement techniques and methods of loading deuterium into palladium.

In the same year on July 22, in the International Hall in Tokyo, the International Electrochemical Society Conference was held. Cold fusion was assigned a special session, but this was, on balance, more of a media event contrived for public relations than a serious scientific forum. I was not impressed. There were six presentations from Japan and six from overseas, featuring Fleischmann, Pons, and Bockris.

The meeting was held in a hall with room for a thousand people, and it was besieged by television cameras and reporters. It was a flamboyant setting which made detailed questions and answers quite impossible. Communication was one-way, from the speaker to the crowd, making it more like a political convention than a physics conference.

The presentations were scheduled to start at 12:30 in the afternoon, with 30 minutes allotted to each speaker. But just before the conference began the sponsors explained that Fleischmann and Pons, who were scheduled first, wanted an hour and a half, and the other ten speakers who were to follow had been cut back to 15 minutes each.

The Japanese speakers flew into a panic. As one of the people in line to speak, I rushed to rearrange my paper and overhead projector slides. I had a dreadful time, but I managed to ad lib my way through the presentation.

At this meeting Fleischmann and Pons reported only that their results were correct and supported by the evidence, adding nothing to what was already published. Still, it is no wonder they adopted this defensive stance. Anyone would. They were forced to give talks at so many different meetings, and pushed into so many press conferences, and on top of that they were sought after at physics conferences and committee hearings. I, too, was treated like some kind of celebrity scientist, "the first in Japan" to successfully replicate cold fusion, merely because I had reported detecting neutrons, which is no big deal and only a minor contribution to the field. If this treatment was all there was to it, I wouldn't mind, but I have also been subjected to a great deal of slander and unfounded accusations. Both good and bad effects continue to this day. Yamaguchi* of NTT and Takahashi also suffered greatly.

There are, of course, people who do not shrink from making sensational claims to attract attention, and there are researchers who think only of making a buck. Thanks to people like this, legitimate researchers are harmed.

A session of the 1989 Japan Physics Society Fall Conference opened on October 12, a Wednesday, at 3:30 in the afternoon, at Miyasaki University. It was an experimental nuclear science symposium at which the theme of "low temperature fusion" was considered. As you see from the seminar title— "low temperature" rather than "cold"—physicists from the start never considered "cold fusion" a legitimate theme. However "muon catalyzed fusion" was an accepted part of physics, so cold fusion was subsumed in that category as "low temperature fusion."

Something happened just two months before that, in August. I got a telephone call from the Physics Society saying they were planning to hold a special session, and they wanted me to participate, an assignment I was delighted to undertake. Although it is customary for the Society to pay the travel and accommodation expenses for invited speakers, the officials explained that of course sufficient funds for *this* purpose would not be made available, so I had to pay out of my own pocket. When I later checked the Conference Program in the Physics Society Journal, my name was not on the list of speakers, and my topic was not listed. Also, I was the only speaker for this session, and the only topic on the agenda was neutron detection, despite the fact that by that time other researchers had reported additional cold fusion effects.

---

*Dr. Eiichi Yamaguchi, NTT Basic Research Laboratories, Kanagawa, Japan

I was given 30 minutes to make my presentation. Before I was able to discuss my conclusions and finish the talk, people ignored the chairman and began asking questions, all but heckling me. A junior scientist from a national research facility said, "You say you are measuring neutrons in the underground lab, but Hokkaido University must have many accelerators around that will cause background noise." He had a bad attitude: he completely refused to listen to what I had to say. The same person kept interrupting with other rude questions and statements like, "Why haven't you done more research?" on this or that, or, "Your claims violate theory." At a normal physics conference, interrupting a speaker with such comments would be unthinkable. And there is a polite way to phrase a question. After the speaker finishes and it is time for questions, it would be appropriate to ask: "How do you deal with noise? How reproducible was the effect? What do you think the mechanism might be?" Unfortunately, these people who make rude comments always seem to show up at physics conferences to bother me when I talk about cold fusion. And not only me: they attack other researchers in this field. I think this is a form of discrimination. I am not singling out the Physics Society unfairly. I have no bone to pick with them. I come from a physics background myself. I have always had a warm spot for the Physics Society and especially for this conference, which produced many fine results in the past. I consider myself a mainstream scientist, and I thought I was of the same mindset as the scientific leaders who organize and run these conferences, which was all the more reason I now felt disappointment and regret.

4

A SERIOUS EXPERIMENT

A Closed Cell

Heavy water is expensive. The cost depends on the purity: 100 grams of 99.75% pure heavy water costs 10,000 yen; 99.8% costs 12,000; and the price of 99.9% pure heavy water shoots up to 15,000 yen. With an open cell at high current, heavy water is consumed at a furious rate. Over a single day at 1 amp, 8.95 grams of heavy water are depleted by electrolysis. Most of the input electricity converts to heat, which heats the electrolyte and causes substantial additional losses from evaporation. In a long experiment lasting months you can use up a kilogram or more.

The worst problem with an open cell is that you must add make-up water to replenish the heavy water. When you do, you cannot avoid disturbing the cell and changing the conditions of electrolysis. Also, you introduce contamination, and you concentrate the contamination already present in the heavy water. (Electrolysis and evaporation are methods of distilling water. Pure water leaves the cell; contamination is left behind in the residue.) To solve these problems, from the time I began the first experiment I planned to try again eventually with a closed cell. In this type of cell, the critical component is the "recombiner"—the material that catalyzes the conversion of free deuterium and oxygen back into heavy water. The choice of materials is straightforward: most people use a platinum recombiner. But you must consider important factors like the recombiner shape; size; position in the cell, and any surface treatments. A mistake in the planning stage can lead to a serious accident later on.

American researchers at SRI International use a closed cell. On January 2, 1992, when Dr. Andrew Riley was moving a cell, an explosion occurred, and the top of the cell struck and killed him. It was made of stainless steel with a Teflon inside lining. The recombiner was made up of aluminum beads coated with platinum. The surface of the beads had become covered with recombined water and they stopped functioning. Because free deuterium and oxygen gas continued to evolve rapidly and the safety valve failed, pressure built up to 30 atmospheres. Then the cell was jolted when the researcher attempted to open it up. This caused the layer of recombined water to fall off the beads. The platinum was exposed, and recombination occurred suddenly, resulting in an explosion. This heart-rending accident caused the sole casualty of cold fusion research to the present day.

Free hydrogen and oxygen mixed in any proportions will explode, but on the other hand, without something to trigger the explosion—a spark or catalyst—they will not readily react. To ensure a reaction will occur you can use platinum black which has been treated to create a rough surface with a large surface area. To ensure the recombiner remains activated, the surface must remain clean. When deuterium and oxygen gas recombine to form heavy water, the reaction produces 244 kilojoules per mole, and you must consider how this heat will be removed from the recombiner. I designed the cell putting safety first, making the reaction vessel out of a stainless steel solid rod, which was 13-cm diameter on the outside to start with. It was machined to form a vessel 20 cm tall, with a 9-cm outside diameter, 7-cm inside diameter. Inside this metal vessel I placed another cell made of 1 cm thick Teflon. Attached to the lid, which was of the same double-layer construction, were several terminals for the temperature and pressure gages. To avoid contamination these parts were thoroughly coated with Teflon, and electric power supply leads to the anode and cathode were made of palladium and platinum, making it, all in all, a terribly pricey "deluxe" model cell.

I had the cell fabricated by Mr. Mori of Santsuri Machine & Tools, who has been making things like this for me for many years. It was designed to operate normally at 150°C and 10 atmospheres, with maximum operating temperature and pressure of 200°C, 150 atmospheres, a large safety margin. Needless to say, the cell was equipped with a safety valve.

The cell was made in October 1989. Of course, just because it was made according to my specifications, that does not mean it worked right off the bat. The first step was a pressure test of the outer cylinder, but it would not do to use hydrogen for this purpose, so I began with nitrogen gas at 5 atmospheres, then 10, then 20 atmospheres, increasing the pressure little by little, ending up at 135 atmospheres. I held the pressure steady at each step for three days and watched for changes. I read the pressure from the electronic transducer installed in the lid. At 10 atmospheres there was absolutely no leak, but at 20 atmospheres there was a small but significant leak, reducing the pressure by 0.2 to 19.8 atmospheres over three days. In other words, the cell leaked 160 cc of nitrogen. I put the cell in a large bucket of water and determined that the leak originated from the power lead junction in the lid. Later I raised the pressure still further and discovered leaks at various other spots, centered around the junctions and ports on the lid, which took me two months to fix. I installed the coil heater around the base of the cell and tested the heating characteristics. I looked at the temperature rise with nitrogen, and I tested to see if high temperatures caused leaks. And indeed, I found a leak when the temperature of the whole cell was raised to 150°C at 50 atmospheres. This turned out to be coming from the Teflon packing in the joint between the lid and the body of the cell. I changed the design of this joint and had the cell machined again, and the leaks finally stopped.

Next came a pressure test with hydrogen at high temperature. Hydrogen at high temperatures is strongly reactive. Exposing the platinum, palladium or stainless steel components to hydrogen would be dangerous, so I began by testing the Teflon inner cell alone, removed from the steel cell body. I was pleased to find I had no problems with the inner cell. I wrapped the coil heater directly around it. I raised the temperature to 100°C and I saw no leaks at 10 atmospheres, so I performed another pressure test of the entire cell with the Teflon inner cell assembled inside the stainless steel outer vessel. At 100°C and 50 atmospheres there was no leak, but above that a gradual leak developed. Gas was coming out of the pressure transducer orifice. I could not determine where the gas escaped from the inner container. Once again I tested the Teflon inner cell alone, using nitrogen. I saw the vessel was swelling slightly, changing shape and leaking out of a crack between the cell and the lid. I took a fresh look at the entire design. I decided to modify the Teflon inner jacket lid, adding a stainless steel reinforcing inner lid. I solved the problem by pressing down on the reinforced Teflon lid, and by making the lower Teflon portion smoother. By this time it was already March 1990. Along the way I ran into other problems I had not bargained for. The palladium electric leads absorbed hydrogen and changed shape, so I had to replace the leads above the water line with platinum.

Next, finally came the platinum recombiner test. To judge recombiner performance I had to confirm that all free hydrogen and oxygen gas in the cell was converted back into water. I selected a platinum mesh because platinum does not absorb hydrogen, so the gas remains a stoichiometric mix. I put distilled water and lithium (0.5 molar LiOH) in the cell. I set the temperature at 30°C, and began electrolysis at 1 ampere. After the first two hours the pressure rose to about 2 atmospheres, then after a few minutes it fell back to one atmosphere, which confirmed that the catalytic recombiner was working with air mixed in the head space. In this case temperature is important; this catalysis begins to work above 50°C. Once it is activated it continues to function in a stable fashion. I selected a piece of platinum 5 cm wide, 20 cm long, woven with a fine 0.1 mm mesh. Here again the price was sky high: 200,000 yen ($2,000). I then folded it and wrapped it around the inside upper portion of the cell. The fat platinum wires held their shape, the recombiner stayed in the correct position.

In this tedious, step by step, painstaking fashion, I fixed various problems until I was at last ready to begin the main experiment. Although there is nothing new about an electrolytic cell, designing and building this one had been tough and getting it to work was a heck of a struggle. The lesson was once again brought home to me just how difficult it is to make a new machine work properly. I think this can be said for any technology. When someone brings you a device that has already been perfected and adjusted in good working condition, you can always learn to operate it. That is easy. You learn the true value of a machine when you design and build it yourself from scratch.

The testing stage was finally over. I was ready to begin the real experiment. By now it was already June; I had spent eight months preparing. I decided to use a large piece of palladium for the cathode. It was a centimeter thick and weighed about 100 grams. If everything went according to plan, when the cathode was fully saturated with deuterium the oxygen pressure inside the cell should not go over 10 atmospheres, leaving a good safety margin.

I began by washing out the vessel. I rinsed it repeatedly with ultra-high grade purified water. Then I filled the cell with this purified water and added lithium to make an LiOD concentrate at 0.5 molar, and I performed electrolysis using only platinum electrodes. I continued for about a week, raising the temperature up to $150°C$. I discarded the liquid that had been in the cell, and this time I put 400 ml of heavy water into the cell. I added enough lithium to make a 0.5 molar LiOD solution. I used high purity reagents from the German company Merck, which it is safe to say contain virtually none of the impurities which might cause problems. Contaminants from all metals combined did not amount to 0.1%. In other words, the total amount of contaminants in the cell was about 10 mg.

The reason I was obsessed with excluding contamination will become clear later, when I describe my efforts to substantiate the occurrence of a large scale nuclear reaction by detecting transmuted reaction products. To succeed in chemistry, you must pay meticulous attention to every detail at every stage. It may seem like a nuisance, but you cannot do valid research without precise preparation.

It was time to prepare the palladium rod, which was the most important step. First I attached a 1 mm platinum electrical lead rod to the fat palladium rod. I spot welded them by pressing the ends of the rods together and passing a high current through both of them. The metal in the parts where the two rods were in contact partially melted, firmly bonding them. Compared with other methods of bonding, this treatment introduces fewer contaminants. Using a piece of quartz glass, I scraped the area around the weld and the part of the rods which had been in contact with tungsten weld-ing electrodes, polishing until it was smooth. After treating it in aqua regia(an acid mix), I put it in a beaker of acetone and washed it many times in an ultrasonic cleaner. Then things got complicated. I put the cathode in a spe-cially prepared aluminum cylinder lined on the inside with a thin sheet of palladium, and I evacuated the aluminum cylinder while raising the temper-ature to 200°C for about a day, to remove gas from the inside and gas adsorbed on the cathode surface. I gripped the cathode with large Teflon tweezers and suspended it in the cell, which was a difficult job. I carefully de-gassed a dummy platinum cathode and installed it in the cell. Then I began initial electrolysis with two platinum electrodes, leaving the palladium electrode present in the cell but without power. The platinum electrode acted as a "getter," removing contamination from the electrolyte, the other elec-trodes, the recombiner, and the cell wall. I set the temperature at 150°C and ran electrolysis at 1 amp for a week. Then I made the palladium electrode positive (an anode) and ran the current for a few hours, to clean the palla-dium. Finally, I removed the dummy platinum cathode and analyzed the accumulated contamination on it.

After finishing this, I removed head space gas from the cell with a vacu-um pump, and I was finally ready to begin the main electrolysis run. I took this closed cell to the underground laboratory for the first time, and began a complex series of experiments. It was already June 1990.

First, I raised the temperature to 130°C using the external heater, and when the temperature stabilized I was able to commence electrolysis. The pressure gradually rose. After ten days had elapsed, pressure was up to 10 atmospheres; after about fifteen days it rose to 13 atmospheres and stabi-lized. Electrolysis was proceeding normally, the deuterium was being absorbed into the palladium, and oxygen was left behind in the head space. Everything about the experiment was going as we had expected it would. Three weeks passed. The neutron flux did not increase as we had hoped. But we did see a distinct 2.45 MeV peak in the spectrum.

We measured the temperature at a steady 140°C. The electric current and pressure also remained stable; nothing appeared to be changing. The current density was 45 mA, or 1.5 amps applied to the total cathode surface area of 33 cm^2. Input voltage was 5 or 6 volts, making total power about 8.4 watts. At 135°C, the cell constant was 0.3°C per watt, so the temperature rise from electrolysis was only 2.5°C.

Plate 16 shows the entire course of the experiment. The lines indicate the pressure, temperature and the concentration of deuterium in the palladium (loading). Electrolysis was performed three times. I ran electrolysis for three weeks, then stopped it for six weeks, in three cycles. With this technique, the metal gradually "softens" and the deuterons go in more easily. I reduced the temperature with each successive cycle from 140 to 105 and then to 75°C, and I determined loading based on the known diffusion behavior for each temperature setting.

The measurements soon revealed several important factors:

1. Deuteron loading density is a function of current density and temperature, and no matter how long electrolysis continues, loading will not exceed a certain value.

2. The absorption and desorption processes were much slower than expected.

3. Neutron emissions were sporadic, and not correlated with changes in temperature, pressure or deuteron loading.

These were my first observations. After the second electrolysis cycle it looked like heat bursts were occurring after electrolysis ceased, in rather long bursts lasting five to six hours, some even longer. This was extraordinary. Unfortunately, because I had not exhaustively calibrated the system to measure heat precisely, I could not formally publish this observation.

Another amazing thing happened. Both heater and electrolysis power were generated by stable, laboratory grade, regulated power supplies, so heating and electrolysis joule heating should have been stable, but after electrolysis began and the cathode was fully loaded with deuterium, temperature and voltage began varying in a periodic cycle. It was approximately 24 hours long. Temperature varied by as much as 10°C. The voltage was also clearly changing from 100 to 103 V, with the low value at around 2:00 p.m. Heat was anticorrelated with voltage, peaking every day at the same time voltage fell.

Several possible causes for this can be considered:

1. The power supply voltage was fluctuating even though the instruments showed it was stable.

2. Ambient temperature changes.

3. Some other source of noise.

4. The effect of loading and deloading of deuterium in the palladium.

5. Daily variation of cosmic rays and the like.

Item (1) was soon discounted, by testing the power supplies with stand-alone meters. Item (2) was not an issue because the ambient temperature in this section of the underground laboratory is virtually the same year-round. Item (3), noise, was not correlated with the cyclical change. In item (4) I determined that there was no correspondence between the temperature change and deuterium loading and deloading; a hypothetical respiration-like phenomenon was not found. This left only item (5), cosmic rays. There are many kinds which have a variety of well-known cycles and fluctuations. A study of cosmic ray intensity cycles shows a peak at midday and a low point at night, correlating well with the cell temperature fluctuations. Roughly estimated, a $10°C$ temperature fluctuation means the corresponding power fluctuation must be well over 10 watts. What kind of cosmic ray could have this effect? Only limited types of rays could reach a cathode inside a thick steel jacket, in a cell buried deep underground. A highly energetic charged particle or a neutral particle with no charge might be considered. Among these, the meson or neutron are likely candidates. We can conjecture that both types would be likely to cause a reaction in the deuterons packed in the palladium lattice, and this reaction might accelerate cold fusion by triggering an avalanche-style reaction. Later, this provided a helpful clue in the search for the reaction mechanism.

We Find Tritium

I was joined by a dynamic new researcher, Kazuhisa Azumi. He was a young, enthusiastic research assistant from Science II (Department Head Sato's group). Like many others, he had been intrigued and inspired by Fleischmann and Pons' announcement of cold fusion. He had stayed in touch with me, and kept up to date on the research, and he soon joined the debate over cold fusion. During the planning phase of the closed cell experiment he offered many ideas, especially regarding the recombiner. After we completed the first series of experimental runs with the closed cell in June 1990, he analyzed a sample of electrolyte. His analysis concentrated on gas, ions, and tritium

At four in the afternoon on February 2, 1991, I got a phone call from Azumi. "Can I come over there? This thing has produced astounding results," he said, clearly excited. Not five minutes later he came dashing in holding two sheets of data. "I have only done the measurement ten times, so I do not know about this for sure yet, but it looks like tritium concentration has increased more than two orders of magnitude," he said, showing me the results from the liquid scintillator. The instrument showed 56,124 counts per minute compared to the background of only 545 counts.

"This sure is an anomalously high value. I'd say the tritium concentration is way up," I said.

Azumi responded, "Well, these are preliminary results. Until various corrections are applied we cannot be sure these are the right values."

I said, "Yeah, well, keep at it for a while before we announce a conclusion. If this were D-D fusion occurring, based only on the number of neutrons we've seen, the tritium should not even be measurable." The two of us began speaking in cautious tones.

We spoke this way because the atmosphere surrounding cold fusion was incomparably worse than it had been at the beginning in 1989. After we announced neutrons, there were many announcements from other teams describing a slight neutron flux, no higher than the level we measured. Most heat results were negative. So we had to be even more cautious than before. Many other people studying cold fusion had learned to keep their mouths shut even when they did get a positive result.

Measuring tritium can be an extremely knotty problem. Tritium is an unstable, radioactive isotope of hydrogen, with two extra neutrons. The half life is 12.3 years, and when it decays it emits a beta particle and turns into an isotope of helium. The trick is to measure that beta particle, but the energy from it is weak, and it does not have a particularly well defined peak, which makes it so hard to detect. Other difficulties include: (1) There might be tritium in the heavy water, palladium, or the cell before the experiment; (2) Liquid scintillators are sensitive to chemical light-emitting reactions from a tiny amount of contamination or material from the detector wall, and produce a light which might be mistaken for tritium. It is also imaginable that contamination might come in during the measurement process. In truth, groups from around the world had already mistakenly reported tritium for these reasons. We ended our discussion by deciding that Azumi would do a series of exhaustive verification experiments to prove this was tritium and to compute a precise value for the tritium concentration.

His determination would be based on five procedures. He would:

(1) Distill a sample of pure water from the electrolyte to eliminate contamination, and he would use the same treatment on a sample of the original heavy water for comparison.
(2) Use different instruments.
(3) Use different kinds of scintillators.
(4) Measure the spectrum.
(5) Measure the half-life.

We soon determined that there was virtually no measurable tritium inside the palladium, in the cell, or in a sample of electrolyte reserved from before the test. We purified the used electrolyte by distilling it in a quartz glass. We analyzed the distillate and the residue. The result, we learned, was that the liquid contained many metal ions, especially palladium and platinum at several parts per million, and these ions did produce powerful chemical luminescence. However, even when we employed the distillate only, and we changed meters or used different scintillators, we still detected large amounts of what appeared to be tritium. The spectrum and the half-life also indicated tritium.

How concentrated was the tritium? How much had been produced? We determined that by comparing the reserved samples to samples of used electrolyte. We found 3×10^{11} atoms of tritium. Total neutrons produced over the course of the experiment was about 4 orders of magnitude lower, roughly 10^6 to 10^7 neutrons. Assuming the remarkable excess heat production was no artifact, it varied from several watts up to about 10 watts, and the entire excess heat release was on the order of 10^6 or 10^7 joules of energy. Comparing the numbers as a whole, the first thing that strikes you is that with ordinary D-D fusion the ratio of neutrons, tritium, and joules of heat would be $1{:}1{:}10^{-12}$, but the ratios derived in this experiment were $1{:}10^{4\text{-}5}{:}10^{-1\text{-}-2}$. Tritium production was 4-5 orders of magnitude larger than conventional fusion. Heat was 12-13 orders of magnitude greater. This result completely bewildered us. Our results were in agreement with those reported from other cold fusion experiments around the world. The measured values varied, but in every case, tritium was five or more orders of magnitude greater than neutron production, and excess heat was ten or more orders of magnitude higher than conventional theory predicts.[3]

The First International Conference on Cold Fusion

This was the state of affairs when the First International Conference on Cold Fusion (ICCF-1) was held in Salt Lake City, Utah, beginning on March 28, 1990. It lasted three days. It was sponsored by the National Institute for Cold Fusion, a Utah state organization, and it featured positive results. Most researchers were from the U.S., with other participants from Japan, India, and Italy, including teams that are still continuing research. There were also papers from researchers who have not reported much since, from England, Switzerland, Spain, Taiwan and Korea. In the year that passed since 1989, the center of the research had broadened from the University of Utah to include Texas A&M University (the Bockris team), Stanford University, Los Alamos National Laboratory, Oak Ridge National Laboratory, and others, and the accuracy of the experiments had greatly improved. Despite the fact that such groups were engaged in the research, reproducibility remained at about 50%, but several dozen groups from all over the world had verified the phenomenon, which was highly significant.

While the conference was focused on research teams reporting positive results, it should not be forgotten that many groups reporting negative results were also represented. A deuteron fusion reaction at room temperature, in the solid state, liquid or gas, is impossible according to conventional theory. There are two possible deuteron fusion reactions: D+D $\rightarrow$ neutron+helium-3 or D+D $\rightarrow$ proton+tritium. At energy levels up to several thousand electron volts the two reactions are equally likely. Thus, for each neutron produced, you would expect one atom of helium-3 (from the first reaction), a proton, and a tritium atom (from the second). Neutrons should equal tritium atoms.

To summarize the results of this conference, excess heat is generally 10^{12} times greater than expected, and tritium is 10^8 more. A particularly noteworthy excess heat result was seen in an experiment performed at Oak Ridge National Laboratory, in which excess heat resulted from prolonged electrolysis with heavy water; the heat was stopped by adding ordinary water. When the water was again replaced with heavy water, the heat gradually built up again. The important point was that when electrolysis was stopped, the heat went away completely, and when the heat was present the power density was 20 watts per cubic centimeter, which is equivalent to the power density of a nuclear reactor fuel rod. Srinivasan* of India's Bhabha Atomic Research Center and researchers at Stanford University both reported large amounts of tritium in the palladium after electrolysis. The larger significance of this conference was the totality of results: after this, it was no longer possible to deny the reality of cold fusion.

The Second International Conference on Cold Fusion

The Second International Conference on Cold Fusion (ICCF-2) was held in Como, Italy in June 1991. This time there were no major changes from the year before. Most researchers had little new to report. I did not attend, but my own experiment had produced a remarkable result.

When I stopped the experiment to open the closed cell and remove the test cathode, I found the surface was entirely covered with a black deposition. (See Plate 6). I could not begin to imagine how so much contamination could have gotten into the cell, or why the surface was so transformed. My obstinate goal was to confirm a D-D fusion reaction, and I wanted to restart the experiment quickly, so the truth is, it never occurred to me to stop and analyze the surface. As far as I could imagine, carbon from the air must have come into the cell and precipitated onto the surface.

*Dr. Mahadeva Srinivasan, (BARC), Bombay, India

I polished the surface again with emery paper, and after removing the black eduction, I washed the cathode in aqua regia (an acid mix) to dissolve away remaining traces. I made a new batch of electrolyte as well, cleaned and purified the platinum anode, the lead wires, the recombiner, and started a new electrolysis experiment.

Much later, after I developed a new hypothesis to explain the phenomenon, I realized that when I scraped off the cathode, I had destroyed critical evidence. It was like throwing away treasure.

An Anomalous Heat Burst

It was March 24, 1991. Exactly two years had passed since I began these experiments. I had changed the experimental conditions, increasing current density by a factor of 4 to 0.2 amperes per square centimeter. Mainly I had in mind the goal of accelerating the reaction. Current was 6 amperes, input voltage was 4 volts, total electric power 24 watts. The power supply was taken from the ion separator I used in my old proton accelerator experiment. It was a superbly stable model, rated at 40 volts, 50 amps. Before commencing electrolysis I raised the temperature of the cell to 75°C with the coil heater. At this time the cell constant was about 1°C per watt, so with 24 watts input the cell temperature rose to about 100°C. At the beginning of the run for some reason the recombiner did not work well, and once every two minutes or so an explosion would occur, abruptly pushing the pressure up to about 30 atmospheres. This condition continued for about three days, after which the recombiner stabilized, the palladium gradually absorbed the deuterium, pressure reached approximately 7 atmospheres, indicating that deuterium loading had reached 95% (D/Pd=0.95).

Two weeks later, on April 6, the temperature slowly rose to between 105 and 110°C, and as it did before it oscillated some 10°C daily. At this time anomalous heat had already started. But the increase was so small I had continued measuring without noticing it. Then on the morning of April 22, I stopped electrolysis and waited for the deuterium in the palladium to deload. Usually, when you stop electrolysis, the deuterium in the palladium deloads quickly and combines with the oxygen in the cell head space, producing heat. I knew this reaction would finish in about ten hours. The palladium I employed weighed 100 grams, which is close to 1 mole (106 grams). If this was fully loaded with 1 mole of deuterium, as the deuterium de-gassed it would produce a half-mole of heavy water, and the total heat release would be 151 kilojoules at most. Divide this by duration and you get 4.2 watts average power. This value is about one tenth of the energy needed for electrolysis, so it should only cause the cell temperature to rise about 2°C. But, even after deuterium deloading subsided, the temperature did not fall below 75°C, remaining instead at 90°C. I realized this was happening on the morning of April 25, when I looked at the data log. To my surprise the temperature was 100°C. Moreover, it was slowly rising. This happened just after 9:00 a.m., when Akimoto stood beside me examining the neutron readings.

"Akimoto," I said, "look at this: the temperature is rising. This is sort of strange. It's 30°C above the calibration point. Do you think the display is calibrated correctly?"

Akimoto responded, "The temperature's going up? Let's see . . . You're right, it sure is," he said, looking at the data trace. "Let me have a look at the neutrons." He flipped through the multichannel data analyzer memory blocks. "Nope, there is no particular change. We still have the same old 2.45 MeV peak. It hasn't gone up significantly. Everything looks about the same," he said as he checked the spectra.

I wondered uneasily if the temperature really was as high as indicated. I removed some of the neutron moderator plastic blocks in front of the cell and I checked directly with meters. The heater power supply current and voltage were steady at 20 V, 3.0 A, just as they had been before electrolysis began, and just as they had remained without the slightest change for a month. Of course this was to be expected, since this was a regulated power supply. The heating coil was covered with stainless steel. Resistance was 6.67 ohms; the coil had been consuming 60 watts for a month. So the temperature should have read 75 degrees. Furthermore, three days had passed since I stopped electrolysis, so by now nearly all of the deuterium should have come out of the metal. The thing is, at this stage I could only measure certain values directly: temperature and pressure, and the voltage and current of the coil heater and electrolysis. I could only infer the deuterium loading level in the palladium, but I had a pretty good idea where it stood based on pressure and temperature.

I put my hand over the surface of the cell, and said: "That's pretty hot. That can't be 70 degrees. It has to be over 100°C. You can't touch it with your bare hand."

"What's happening?" asked Akimoto.

"I don't know. But the deuterium has not come out of the metal; this heat isn't from recombination. And heater power is still at 60 watts."

"Maybe this is the cold fusion effect everyone's talking about."

"It can't be! Electrolysis has been turned off. It's been off for three days. Even cold fusion doesn't do that, as far as I know. In any case, I think it would be best to turn off the heater. If we leave it in this state there is no telling how much higher the temperature will go. If anything bad happens, they'll never let us continue with this research. An accident would be disastrous. Also, those explosions we saw at the beginning of the run bother me. They pushed the pressure well over 100 atmospheres. They recurred hundreds of times." I was terribly worried.

Akimoto said, "Hold on, isn't this a good opportunity? We have been experimenting for more than two years, and we are finally getting some honest to goodness heat. I think we should leave it as is, and see what develops."

"Okay, I'm with you. But if something goes wrong here, in this lab, it would be particularly awkward, so let's move the cell. And let's keep an eye on the temperature," I concluded.

I went back to my lab and brought some rags and towels, and I wrapped the cell in them. Carefully not touching the metal parts, I carried the cell from the underground lab to my own laboratory on the third floor, and I put it behind a heavy metal panel. I thought there would be little danger no matter what happened, since the cell was blocked by the panel. I had other reasons to feel confident: the cell design was rated at 250 atmospheres, and although the Teflon might leak, the stainless steel portion of the cell would not fail even at temperatures over 500°C. And of course the lid had an emergency relief valve. At pressures above 100 atmospheres the gas would automatically vent. But I still felt uneasy. I was not confident the cell could survive a sudden explosion. For many years I had studied the effects of metal that had been exposed to hydrogen at high pressures and temperatures, so I thought I understood vessel design well enough to ensure safety. The truth was that with such a totally unpredictable phenomenon, I was afraid that my knowledge might prove inadequate.

I left the cell on a steel platform. The next day the temperature had not fallen a bit. That was a Friday before a long holiday week. I was afraid to leave the cell in this state, so I made up my mind I would try to cool it. I filled a large plastic bucket with water and partially submerged the cell in it. I noted the temperature by directly measuring the voltage of the sensor, a thermocouple attached to the cell lid. Voltage was 4.0 mV, or 100°C converted to degrees. It was the same as it had been. Even though I had turned off the heater and stopped electrolysis, the heat output maintained itself at 120 watts. After electrolysis was turned off, total heat energy output had reached 1.2×10^7 joules. After I submerged the cell in the bucket of water, the temperature fell rapidly, dropping to about 60°C after an hour. I figured the temperature would continue to fall under these conditions, so I left it, and went home.

The next morning I felt anxious as I arrived at the lab, and astounded when I saw the bucket. The water, which had been around eight-tenths full, was nearly all evaporated, and the temperature had once again risen to around 80°C. By now I was used to weirdness in the lab, but this really threw me. It took 2×10^7 joules to evaporate the water in the bucket (nearly 9 liters). Given the small size of the cell, this energy could not be the heat of combustion or any other chemical transformation. Generally speaking, a chemical heat source of this mass will produce on the order of 10^5 joules by the most generous estimate, so the energy expended in evaporation alone was already two orders of magnitude beyond chemistry. At that point I decided to get a big 20-liter bucket. I filled it with 15 liters of water, enough to completely submerge the cell. When I returned to have a look three days later on April 30, the water had again evaporated. The waterline was below the cell, and the cell temperature was 50°C. For the second time I filled the bucket with 15 liters of water. I recorded the temperature again in my log book by measuring the thermocouple output, and I left the cell. I added 5 liters on May 1, and again on May 2. Then on May 7 when the holiday ended, the water was about half gone, the temperature had declined to 35°C, and the temperature fluctuations had stopped.*

When I began the experiment, I never thought it would be necessary to keep precise calorimetric data, so unfortunately I can only infer how much heat the cell had produced based on factors like the amount of water that evaporated.

Total heat of evaporation after April 30 came to 8.2×10^7 joules. Add to this the heat generated by the cell before that time, and the net total is at least 1.14×10^8 joules, a whopping amount of excess heat. The energy used in electrolysis and the coil heater was 2.6×10^8, or 40% of the excess heat, and all but a tiny fraction of that was immediately expended as heat as electrolysis progressed. It was not stored as a hydride or in any other form of chemical fuel. My estimation of excess heat is very conservative.

Whenever I consider this anomalous heat, I remain astounded at the unpredictability and profundity of the natural world. I have learned a valuable lesson from this experience. I am appalled at my own inability to completely shrug off the bounds of conventional knowledge. Weak as they were, I verified neutron production. I even detected tritium, although the figures

---

*The only source of chemical energy in the cell is the deuterium in the palladium. The cell contains no other chemically active substances, no oxygen, and no fuel. Extensive chemical changes were not seen after the experiment; no ash was found. If the 100 gram palladium was replaced with octane, which is one of the most energy dense chemicals, and the cell was filled with oxygen instead of water, it would produce 4.6×10^6 joules.

did not add up to tritium "commensurate" with the neutrons. But, in my heart, I still harbored the view that the excess heat phenomenon surely could not occur and, for that reason, I had not made adequate preparations to measure it. When the heat did appear, I was totally ill-equipped to deal with it appropriately. You never know when this heat will appear; later I experienced it many times.

The Third International Conference on Cold Fusion

The Third International Conference on Cold Fusion (ICCF-3) was held at the Nagoya International Conference Center from October 21, 1992, lasting 5 days. The highlight of the conference was the presentation by Yamaguchi of NTT.

This research was noteworthy because Yamaguchi made progress using a completely different approach from the conventional heavy water electrolysis method used by most other researchers. Yamaguchi begins with a palladium foil (3 x 3 x 0.1 cm) coated with manganese oxide on one side. The foil absorbs deuterium gas, and then it is cooled. After that the other side is coated with a 200 angstrom thin film of gold and treated to prevent the deuterium gas from escaping. When a current is passed through the foil, a sudden release of heat causes the sample to bend, helium is detected, 3.0 MeV and 4.6 to 6.0 MeV protons are released. When the experiment was performed with hydrogen, Yamaguchi reported that nothing was produced. This was considered a major turning point. It was viewed as epochal proof that a fusion reaction exists. Readers should learn about Yamaguchi's work by all means. I highly recommend his paper.[4]

Other papers that made a strong impression on me included studies showing the effect of loading on excess heat production in palladium, and research with proton conductors, which is not based on aqueous electrolysis. At this conference I, too, reported in detail on the effect of deuterium loading on the amount of excess heat produced when temperature and current density were changed.

I did not report on the May 1991 excess heat burst I experienced after terminating electrolysis, because I did not have precise data. I described results from a subsequent experiment in a poster session display. Other reports were made of heat after electrolysis was turned off (so-called "heat-after-death"), an important point which I think indicates the effect is reproducible.

5

EXPERIMENTS WITH SOLID STATE PROTON CONDUCTORS

Proton Conductors

I wanted to reproduce the excess heat I had observed after electrolysis ceased (a phenomenon now called "heat-after-death"). I decided that a practical way to do this would be to synthesize the mix of elements found inside a palladium cathode. The idea was to increase the concentration of deuterons and enhance excess heat production. I was preoccupied with the first step: increasing overpotential.

Overpotential is complicated. It takes a certain minimum level of energy to break down the water molecules in the solution, separating the deuterons and oxygen atoms. "Overpotential" refers to the energy beyond that minimum threshold. The more of this extra energy you apply, the greater the pressure exerted by the deuterons entering the cathode. Pressure is logarithmically scaled to overpotential, so it is thought that if you can create high overpotential this will create tremendous pressure. This ratio is expressed in the famous Nernst equations, familiar to all electrochemists. But to determine true pressure under extremely high overpotential, this equation cannot be applied in its rudimentary form, as we explained in detail in a recent paper.[5]

To enhance deuteron pressure, you can:

1. *Increase current density.*
   - something many researchers had already done.
2. *Put additives in the heavy water solution.*
   - this affects the way the reaction occurs.
3. *Add other elements to the cathode metal.*
   - I had been attempting this in my research for quite a while, although I had not achieved the results I hoped for.
4. *Change conditions in the metal with surface treatments.*
   - We later determined this is critically important.

I devoted every spare minute to experiments. In May 1992 I was excited by something I saw on the pages of a scientific supply catalog. It described a type of solid state electrolytic ceramic device called a proton conductor, which could be used at temperatures above 1,000°C. The conductors can be loaded with hydrogen ions diffused with an electric field.

In the experiments up to this point, I used a palladium cathode and platinum anode, with ions from a heavy water electrolyte solution. The solid state conductor works on the same principle, except that the device itself acts as both electrolyte and cathode. When metal contacts are placed on either side of the device and current is run through it, it conducts and moves ions into the material just as a cathode does. Proton conductors move hydrogen ions. A wide variety of proton conductors have been developed.[6]

I thought that if proton conductors could be made to generate heat, they would be ideal for this application. In practical applications they would be very effective since they work at high temperatures, which are known to promote the cold fusion reaction. (Carnot efficiency would also be enhanced.) Various different proton conductors are available. These different types would presumably yield different products, which would help elucidate the mechanism of cold fusion. Best of all, proton conductors should load and react quickly. With palladium electrolysis, forcing the deuterons into the lattice requires days or even weeks, but proton conductors operate at high temperatures which increases deuteron mobility, so I thought the reaction might turn on in several minutes or perhaps a half-hour.

Most people believe that the key to successful cold fusion with palladium is to achieve high loading. It is said that when the ratio of deuterons and palladium atoms approach one-to-one, or full saturation, the cold fusion reaction should begin. Yet even when you take extreme measures to increase temperature, pressure, and current density, and you put additives in the electrolyte, you can push loading closer and closer to saturation. But often, despite this, the cell generates only insignificant heat or no heat at all. By this time I had come to believe that high loading may not be such a decisive factor after all. Perhaps a completely different mechanism was at work. I had grown increasingly doubtful that cold fusion can be anything like an ordinary D-D reaction, because the neutrons and tritium are so far out of balance compared to excess heat, and because no matter how tightly you pack deuterons in palladium, the deuteron nuclei remain much too far apart for nuclear fusion to occur. What to make of this? What about the neutrons, tritium and excess heat that *did* evolve from the reaction? These questions were never far from my thoughts while I conducted experiments. I had to devise a working hypothesis. It was pathetic to go on doing electrolysis in a

Plate 1. Neutron generator. The orange box-shaped part on the right is the ion source. Voltage is applied, accelerating the ions to the left, where they strike the target mounted in the blue, left hand portion. This is a 1961 Cockcroft-Walton type deuteron accelerator, made by Toshiba.

Plate 2. Control unit for neutron generator. This is around 10 meters from the main unit. Here I worked day and night.

Plate 3. The entrance to the Hokkaido University Engineering Department 45 MeV linear accelerator building. Inside here, well underground in a chamber off in the corner, we set up the neutron energy analysis system.

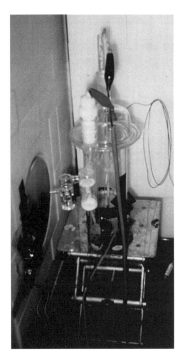

Plate 4. The first electrolysis cell I used, made of glass. It is placed in front of a scintillation neutron detector. The white blocks around it are polyester, to slow down or absorb neutrons.

Plate 5. The completely closed cell. Attached to the top portion (the lid) are the electric power lead terminals and the temperature and pressure gauges. A heating coil is wrapped around the bottom portion of the cell, used to raise the temperature. This is done to study the reaction at high temperatures. (Made by Santsuri Machine & Tools Co.)

Plate 6. Pd and Pt electrodes after electrolysis. Both electrodes are blackened, and the Pd electrode is bent.

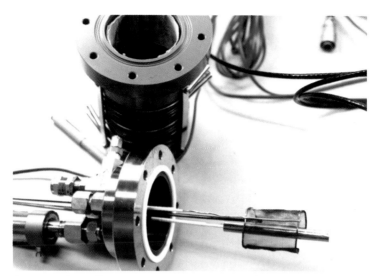

Plate 7. The cell contents. In the core of the cell the platinum recombiner can be seen. The top of the cell has been removed and placed sideways on the table. The palladium rod (10 mm in diameter, length 10 cm), and the platinum anode can be seen. Most cold fusion cells works like a ship-in-a-bottle: components are attached to the lid (except, in this case, the recombiner).

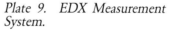

Plate 8. Finished proton conductor. A ceramic, yet at high temperatures it becomes permeable to hydrogen ions.

Plate 9. EDX Measurement System.

Plate 10. The first proton conductor reaction chamber. The inside is visible through the acrylic window. (Made by Hokusan Co.)

Plate 11. Improved proton conductor reactor system. The top portion is the stainless steel reaction vessel, the bottom is the vacuum exhaust. (Made by Tanaka Chemical Corp.)

Plate 12. Inside the reactor vessel. To be resistant to high temperature hydrogen, parts are made of stainless steel, platinum and various ceramics. (Made by Santsuri Machine & Tools Co.)

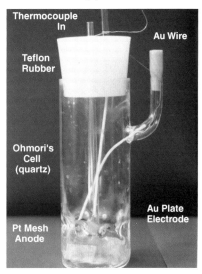

Plate 13. Ohmori cell.

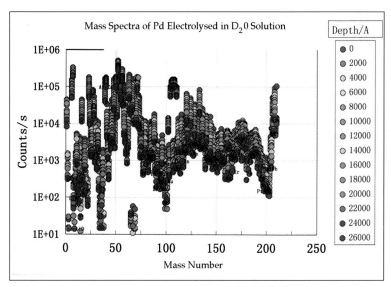

Plate 14. An example of a spectroscopic analysis of a palladium surface. Colors represent depth from surface (in angstroms).

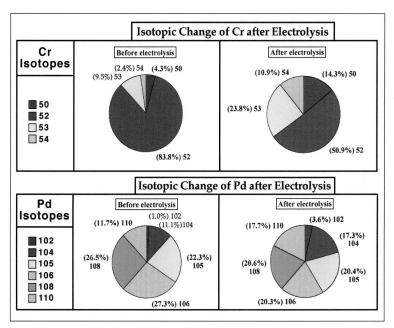

Plate 15. Changes before and after electrolysis with Cr and Pd. Isotopic abundances in percentage are shown in pie charts. For Cr, natural and post-electrolysis abundances are shown (because there was no significant Cr in the sample before electrolysis). For palladium, abundances before and after are shown.

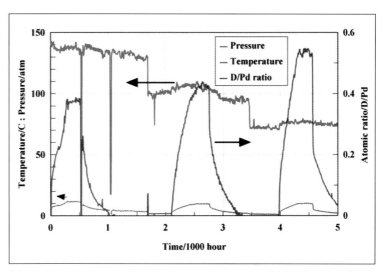

Plate 16. Changes in pressure, temperature and D/Pd ratio during electrolysis (44 mA/cm²). The temperature was changed three times, from 140, to 105, to 75°C while electrolysis was performed. X axis label: Hours x 1000; left Y axis: Temperature /°C : Pressure / atmospheres; right Y axis: the concentration of deuterium in the Pd, D/Pd.

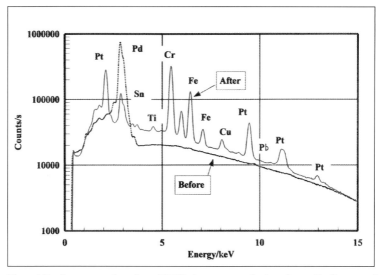

Plate 17. An example of an EDX element analysis of a palladium rod after it produced excess heat during electrolysis. Results from before and after electrolysis are shown. In the palladium rod after electrolysis, all sorts of elements are observed.

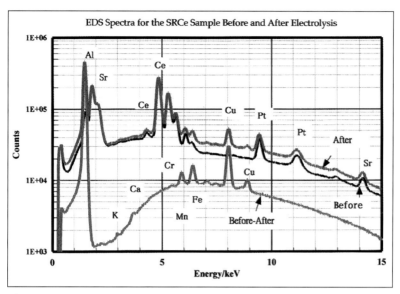

Plate 18. An example of element analysis performed with an EDX on a proton conductor before and after electrolysis. Peaks for K, Ca, Mn, Fe, Ni and Cu are seen.

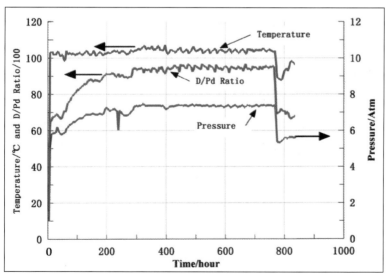

Plate 19. Changes in D/Pd ratio, temperature and pressure during electrolysis; 0.2A/cm^2, 0.5 mol LiOD.

Plate 20.
John O'M. Bockris
and Tadahiko
Mizuno.

Plate 21. Masao Araki of
Nissho Iwai Corporation.

Plate 22. Tadahiko Mizuno.

haphazard fashion, hoping for a positive result—it was more like placing a bet than doing research. I wanted to experiment with something I could control. My first thought was to vary the movement of the deuterons themselves. Proton conductors seemed best suited for this purpose.

I began by investigating different materials. I determined that strontium and cerium devices fall within the right operating temperature range, and they are both notably stable in hydrogen. After I assembled the raw materials, the next thing to consider was how to fabricate the samples. The materials were in fine powder form; shaping and sintering them successfully required continual trial and error. I was making small disks, about the size of a ten-yen coin. I shaped the powder by pressing it into a mold. I sintered the disks in an electric furnace at 1400°C for about one day. After removing them from the furnace I put platinum lead membranes on both sides and the samples were then ready. Writing it out like this makes it sound simple, but the samples often came loose from their molds, and would often break during the sintering phase. Sometimes the surface would be too uneven, making the sample unusable. I experienced repeated failures. It took a year before I finally mastered the technique.

The experimental apparatus, shown in the photograph (see Plate 10), was made from the cooling chamber originally used in a deuteron beam irradiation experiment. It is filled with deuterium gas. I put a joule heater inside this copper reaction chamber to keep it hot, because proton conductors do not function at room temperature. They do not begin to conduct electricity until the temperature is raised to several hundred degrees. The starting, baseline temperature of the calorimeter was high, and any excess heat would make it even higher. The sample proton conductor was mounted on a holder inside, sandwiched between two platinum electric leads, with a thermocouple in direct contact with the conductor to monitor temperature changes. When an electric current is passed through the platinum leads, deuterons are carried into the proton conductor. I thought that if I could force enough deuterium into the conductor, a cold fusion reaction would occur, and I thought that by varying the power, the alternating current oscillations, temperature, and other factors, I might control the reaction—if one occurred in the first place. By the time I set about doing the experiment it was already 1993 (See Plate 10). I performed a few dozen runs, and observed several clear instances of excess heat.

Continued Anomalous Heat

The research had begun progressing smoothly by June 4, 1993. In the runs leading up to this experiment I varied the composition and thickness of the strontium, cerium, yttrium, and the thickness of the platinum membrane until I was finally able to get a stable result. I tested one sample out of a batch. I placed it in the electric furnace and heated it to 1400 °C in air to make the platinum film firmly attach to the conductor. Then I gradually lowered the temperature to 400°C and admitted deuterium gas into the chamber to see how stable the conductor was when it took up deuterium. One day when I performed this test an extraordinary thing happened. The sample color suddenly changed from dark red, to red, to yellow—a clear indication that the temperature was shooting up. The heat increased, the sample glowed white, and after ten or twenty seconds it began to melt. I thought this must be a reaction to the deuterium. In a panic I ran the vacuum pump to remove the deuterium gas, and the temperature gradually dropped. It was a quick reaction just as I had hoped for, but I could no longer ignore the fact that this research was potentially hazardous.

When the sample cooled, I examined it, and I saw that the aluminum holder beneath it had also partially melted and fused into the melted edge of the sample itself, which now looked like a lump of taffy. The melting point of both the sample and the aluminum was above 1500°C, which meant that in ten or twenty seconds the temperature climbed more than a thousand degrees. I realized I would have to be cautious in future experiments, because I did not have good control over the reaction. I saw partial melting on several occasions after that.

I proceeded to do additional experiments with proton conductors of the same composition and shape as the one that produced the large burst of heat. Although I replicated as closely as I could, out of twenty samples I got clear cases of excess heat only about three times. The problem was how to identify the difference between samples which would produce heat and ones which would not, so subsequent research was mainly oriented toward materials analysis.

The Fourth International Conference on Cold Fusion

I prepared a presentation of my proton conductor results for the Fourth ICCF meeting. This conference was held on the Hawaiian island of Maui at the Lahaina Hyatt Regency, a typical resort hotel. It lasted four days, from December 6 to December 9, 1993. Two hundred fifty people attended from some thirteen countries, and in its own way it was a sparkling success. But I got the impression there were no truly outstanding results, and no major changes from the previous meeting.

ICCF-4 Impressions

I was not able to attend every lecture and read every paper presented that week. But I did have a chance to hear the key lectures. It was clear that the major research groups, like Fleischmann and Pons, Jones, Fritz Will, and Bockris had nothing new to report, and they were merely repeating what they said at ICCF-2 and ICCF-3. Jones' presentation in particular made one wonder whether he was serious about doing research. He presented slides that looked like they were part of a tour guide, and he retracted his previous claims of a weak neutron flux from cold fusion. He turned completely about-face, claiming instead that the neutrons must have originated from radioactive contamination in the sample. Many researchers had concluded that neutron claims are extremely weak and doubtful at best, so perhaps he decided to go with the flow. It is not clear whether he had some ulterior motive, but in any case his presentation had a weird feel to it.

The conference as a whole was uninspiring, but I was encouraged by reports of excess heat from solid state electrolyte proton conductors similar to my own. Perhaps it is natural that others doing this research would arrive at the same conclusions and use the same approach I did.

Overall, the presentations were a mixed bag. Many of the papers seemed frivolous. They detracted from serious research and distressed serious researchers. But, you must not judge papers too harshly on first impressions, or you run the risk of excluding some that turn out to be novel and creative. This should be avoided in the early stages of development in a new scientific field. I think we can anticipate a gradual improvement in our understanding of where we are headed, after a period of repeated trial and error experimentation. I think we Japanese, and I myself, have a tendency to rush things along. We have an aversion to devoting time to planning and reconsidering. We should refrain from jumping to conclusions.

Papers presented at this conference included: 38 about excess heat; 43 on nuclear effects; 23 on materials; and 45 about theory, the most popular subject. People reported measuring excess heat in 35 cases; neutrons in 19 cases, tritium in ten cases; helium in seven; mostly nuclear effects based on conventional fusion. But there was clearly also a new trend, especially from Russia and Ukraine, which included ten surprising reports of transmutation. I think this group of reports provides an important hint about the future direction of cold fusion research. Sure, their presentations were anything but slick: they have trouble with English, some require translators to give their talks, their slides and viewgraphs were amateurish, but the papers were a creative departure from cold fusion research as it has been done until now, and an important indicator of future trends.

During this conference I learned about the research of Tadayoshi Ohmori who is also at Hokkaido University, in the Catalysis Research Center. Later, we collaborated.

I gave my presentation on December 7, at 4 p.m. As always happens when I lecture, I found the allotted 20 minutes passed before I knew it and I was out of time. Many people asked questions when I finished, perhaps because my presentation was about something new, a departure from palladium electrolysis in heavy water. I had time to address questions from five people. Typically they wanted to know which type of sample materials produced excess heat. As often happens in cold fusion, I could not say. I do not know enough to characterize the material.

I gave my talk in a small meeting hall with room for about 50 people. The room seemed full, people were crowding in and standing in the back, which made me realize that interest in this field has not faded. The chairman of my session was Bockris, who I had not seen in a while. He looked as youthful and vigorous as ever. Something else I remember which made a big impression on me was seeing eminent electrochemist Richard Oriani* listening intently to my presentation, and nodding agreement. He is a researcher as famous as Bockris in metal hydrides and corrosion. Although he has officially retired from the University of Minnesota where he had established the corrosion research laboratory, he continues to do as much research as a full time professor. He has been deeply interested in cold fusion from the start, and he has attempted many replication experiments, reporting negative results more often than positive ones. Of course he was performing rigorous experiments, and under the conditions that prevailed, most results were negative. Things are not much different today. If you limit your goal to finding the products of D-D fusion: (neutrons, tritium, heat and helium), anyone can see you will not achieve much. This was why the search for products has changed, and the focus is now on transmutation, as we shall see in later chapters.

Soon after he returned home from the conference, Oriani wrote me a letter. He soon became deeply involved with replication experiments using my proton conductors.

Support for this Research

I would like to digress from the story of the research itself, and touch upon the subject of support from other people, which is so essential for success in any venture.

*Prof. Richard A. Oriani, University of Minnesota, Minneapolis, Minnesota

In the interior of China, in the desolate, desert wastelands, most of the land is mountainous, and difficult to grow crops on. A Japanese man went to live in this territory determined to plant trees, cover the land with forest, and change the environment. Because of his efforts, and after considerable hardships, a great forest now grows there. His words made a deep impression on me. He said: "What I want most from people is for them to work with their hands. Come and plant a tree with me. If you cannot do that, lend me your mind: teach me how to do things; give me your knowledge. If you cannot do that, I would like you to contribute cash. The important thing is to make some contribution in a form you can see with your own eyes."

You can say the same for any field. My research is no exception. It would be unimaginable for me to try to do this research all by myself. I have depended upon help from many people to get where I am today. It goes without saying I have depended upon my collaborators, and the conferences and interchange with other researchers worldwide has also been a vital necessity.

Many people from outside the field have made strong contributions to my work. I would like to mention one of them in particular.

It was April 1991, the second year after I began this research. I got a message from a professor in the law school saying that someone would very much like to meet me, and could I accommodate him. I asked for details, and heard he was Masao Araki, advisor to the Nissho Iwai Corporation. My knowledge of Nissho Iwai was limited to the Lockheed bribery scandal, not a particularly inviting image. I had strong doubts, wondering what a person from a company like that would want with me. Mr. Araki was said to have served as high as vice president, later working in an advisory capacity. But, in any case, I thought I would not judge the man until I had met him, so we arranged a meeting. Eventually, on the first day of May, a large black sedan pulled into the main gate of the engineering department buildings, and a distinguished looking gentleman, who was unlike anything I had expected, alighted.

Masao Araki was an Imperial Naval cadet, graduating as an expert in anti-submarine warfare. He was a seasoned veteran who had traveled widely throughout the world. On the day the war ended he was in Keelung, Taiwan. After that he spent a year and a half traveling around South East Asia in mine sweeping operations, before he was finally able to finish up his duties and return to Japan. He soon joined the Nissho Iwai trading corporation where he dealt with textiles. After a period overseas he switched to working in the petroleum industry. In that capacity he traveled all over the world, searching for energy resources. Given his background, he was extremely apprehensive, about Japan's energy situation, so he got in touch with me on his own personal initiative. He had the idea that this research might just play a major role in Japan's energy future. We met and spoke several times after that, which led to him offering wholehearted support for my research. During the course of his work, he had developed a wide circle of acquaintances and considerable influence. Above all, Araki has a gallant and courageous spirit, coupled with the childlike curiosity and sense of adventure which typifies old-fashioned, traditional Japanese values.

The climate of support for cold fusion at that time was at rock bottom. People refused to treat it as a legitimate branch of science. Researchers having anything to do with it were subjected to all-out censure and criticism. Yes, of course they still are, but it was even worse then, as all sources of research funding had been cut off, official support which scientists rely on had been denied. Most people who had been trying to do cold fusion research had given up, and the few who were continuing were paying for the research out of their own pockets. Araki was shocked and apprehensive when he saw the situation researchers had been placed in. He set to work at once. He took upon himself the difficult task of persuading government officials and industrial managers to support the research. Thanks to his kind offices, less than a year later MITI (Ministry of International Trade and Industry) took positive action in beginning the New Hydrogen Energy Research Project (NHE). As a result, it has been possible to support research not only in Japan, but in all parts of the world. Araki has never sought publicity for his involvement; he has always worked behind the scenes. A lot of credit will be due to him if this research succeeds. He will forever be regarded as the man who provided much-needed resources at a critical time. *

---

*Unfortunately, the NHE program turned out to be a fiasco which collapsed in 1998. Araki was distressed at the turn of events. He and others are still working to salvage the situation. The equipment from the NHE project has been handed over to the universities, where good progress is still being made.

6

NEW DEVELOPMENTS

Oriani's Experiment

It was New Year's Day 1994. I thought about the Hawaii conference and the many questions raised there. I became interested in products from reactions other than the D-D reaction. To research these products, I would have to start by rigorously excluding contamination from sources inside and outside of the cell. I would have to substantially modify the reactor and the instrumentation. I had to select materials with a high melting point, resistivity to oxidation, and those which would not deteriorate when exposed to hydrogen. All components in the cell would have to withstand temperatures as high as 700~800°C. Basically, stainless steel would do the job, but I had to stay alert to prevent problems with the inside finish, and problems with oxidation, reduction, and the release of contaminant gas.

The new cell was ready in April 1994. The biggest improvement in my new experiment was the data collection system. It was automatic, it allowed considerably more detailed analysis, and it was strikingly faster: about a hundred times faster than the manual methods I had relied on previously. Thanks to the speed, I could assess a sample in a single day and do a much more detailed analysis. This had great practical significance; I could change parameters any number of times to zero in on the target phenomenon. I relied on my colleague Kitaichi for this automation. He is superb at circuit design and computer programming. Thanks to his cooperation I was able to make qualitative improvements.

With my new system, I measured the effects of deuterium gas, hydrogen gas, and inert gases, as well as oxygen and nitrogen, mixing and changing them in various ways. I altered many specific factors like the sample composition, morphology, and the metal coating. By making these measurements I came to understand which samples would produce the most excess heat. Depending on the sample, sometimes I found that by changing pressure or the alternating current frequency, I could make the flow of electric current gradually increase. Sometime it would shoot up suddenly, the temperature would rise, and the sample would partially melt or be completely destroyed. I assumed the current was concentrated in the part that melted, but it turned out that was not the only reason. I later analyzed these melted parts and ascertained many anomalous phenomena. Although they were weak, I confirmed low energy X-rays emanating from the samples after electrolysis, and I observed accumulations of elements that should not have existed, all of which indicated that a fascinating and mysterious nuclear reaction had occurred.

After ICCF-4, Oriani from the University of Minnesota contacted me many times as he set about replicating my hydrogen proton conductor experiments. He employed a calorimetry technique entirely different from mine. I used a thermocouple to measure gas temperature in the middle of the chamber. This is simple, but it is dependent upon calibrations, and various problems can affect the measurement, as Oriani understood. For example, when you assemble the cell inside a stainless steel cylinder, and you place the thermocouple above the sample to measure the temperature, you measure a local temperature at one spot. If a tiny amount of air leaks into the cell, it can change the conductivity of the gas and cause a false reading. The thickness and the shape of the sample might have an effect. However, I had performed extensive calibrations to account for these factors, and at this point I had absolutely no problems. But this method would not work well for another researcher unless he first gained considerable experience.

Oriani's method circumvented these problems. He used a Seebeck-style envelope calorimeter, with 700 thermocouples linked in series around the outside of the cell. The integrated value from all thermocouples indicated the temperature. He left a calibration heater turned on at all times, placing it next to the cell. This eliminates major sources of error, and allows an absolute measure of heat. His preparations took more than a year, and it was not until January 1995 that Oriani was able to set about performing the main experiment. It was not until a year after that, on March 20, 1996, that he contacted me to say that he had observed excess heat from some of the sample proton conductors I had sent him.

Later that year he would present his final results at the Sixth International Conference on Cold Fusion.[7]

Reaction Products

In the proton conductor experiments, some samples work and some do not, and the biggest problem is to determine the differences between the two. Before I left for the Hawaii conference, I was busy with an analysis I hoped would shed light on this problem. I was looking at the structure and quality of the materials. In my 1994 experiments, I not only looked for excess heat, I also focused on differences in the distribution of elements, and the effect of changing the ratio of strontium to cerium. In May of that year I asked Kurokawa in the High Temperature Chemistry Department to do some studies of post-experiment samples using energy dispersive X-ray spectroscopy (EDX). He called me one day to tell me he was ready to begin the measurements, so I should come and have a look.

The man on the street has probably never heard of an EDX, but to scientists who analyze elements it is a familiar old friend. With this instrument, electrons strike the surface of the sample, and depending on which elements it contains, distinctive X-rays are produced. The X-ray spectrum reveals what is in the sample. The sensitivity is not particularly good, but the method is simple and it allows a quantitative analysis.

To operate the EDX, you mount the sample in a holder and insert the holder in a chamber through the window in the bottom of the machine (See Plate 9). Then you press a control lever to evacuate the chamber. After a few minutes when the vacuum is high enough, you press a switch on the electric gun and the electron microscope turns on. An image of the surface appears on the screen. It looks bumpy, like the surface of the moon. You increase magnification: 100, 200, 500, 1000, 2000. It is like watching through the window of a lunar lander as it approaches the surface. At that point you press the button turning on the high voltage analysis function, press the data collection button, and on the EDX screen many peaks vigorously spring up. Each peak corresponds to an isotope of an element, and you can quickly identify which is which by observing the energy value of the peak.

"2.08 KeV, that's platinum" said Kurokawa, pointing out the peak on the screen. (See Plate 8.) "9.46, 11.16, 12.96. These are all platinum. They are all weak. These are cerium isotopes: 4.86, 5.3, 5.66."

I commented, "There are no changes here, so we must be looking at the thin film platinum connector."

"Yeah, I guess so," Kurokawa responded. "Okay, let's look at some other area," he said, twisting a control knob. The screen image moved continuously. Something that looked like a volcanic crater came into view. "Let's look at this part," he said, pressing the spectrum reset button to restart data collection.

"The platinum is gone. It looks like cerium and strontium are a lot stronger," said Kurokawa.

"Y'got peaks at 6.4 and 8.0 KeV. Give it a little more time . . . See? It gradually comes in clearer. This would be iron and copper, wouldn't it?" I said.

"Yeah. It looks like you've got a whole lot of other stuff too. It would be best to put it in another instrument, for confirmation. We have an EPMA over at our lab; let's check out the distribution with it."

"Could you do that for me? I have my own EDX, I'll try looking at more samples," I replied.

This was how I first recognized the importance of isotopic distribution. But at that time, I thought of the problem in terms of whether structural differences and contamination (dopants) would cause heat or prevent it. I still did not accept the idea that electrolysis could be causing a nuclear reaction. Not only that, I tended to deny the possibility.

I spent all of 1994, day after day, measuring heat and then analyzing the materials from proton conductors. In the samples that exhibited the sudden temperature rise, in the areas where the reaction occurred, there were clearly anomalous concentrations of chromium, nickel, and other elements which we observed with the EPMA and EDX detectors. I reported these results at the First International Low Energy Nuclear Reactions Conference (ILENR1) at Texas A&M University in June 1995.

In the first part of that year I did some experiments to investigate something which had been bothering me for a long time: radioactivity in samples after electrolysis. If a nuclear reaction occurs, it is common sense to assume that it will create radioactive products. In 1993, Koichi Inoda, a technician with the Nuclear Engineering Department, examined palladium cathodes for radioactive products, and found nothing. However, the sample he tested had been electrolyzed more than a year previously, so short-lived radioisotopes would all be gone. I had a bad feeling that was the reason he saw nothing. Inoda used a germanium detector to look at the gamma spectrum. He was the one who showed me how to operate the accelerator when I was a student. An expert in measuring radiation, he specialized in detecting weak radioactive materials in the atmosphere.

With a proton conductor you can look for radioactivity as soon as electrolysis finishes, so I thought I might find something. Results were unclear, but I realized that in rare cases, after electrolysis with ceramics or palladium, occasionally very low energy, weak X-rays were detected.[8]

On the way back from Texas, Ohmori and I visited Oriani's lab at the University of Minnesota. Minneapolis is a beautiful city near Canada, in an area with many lakes, that was once covered by glaciers. The upper reaches of the deep Mississippi river flow past the campus. I was impressed by the old, historical buildings mixed in with the new city.

Oriani had put together his own calorimeter to test the proton conductors, which I found surprising, because after all, he is more than 70 years old. In Japan it would be unthinkable for a retired professor to work as hard as a full time professor. Oriani asked me many questions about measuring techniques and corrections, and data interpretation. They were the kinds of questions a person would never know to ask without the experience of actually doing the experiment himself.

The day after we arrived in Minnesota, Ohmori and I gave lectures and we answered many questions. During this trip I had the opportunity to consult with Ohmori at length about his experiment. Ohmori is six years older than I. He graduated from the same university and he is an assistant professor at the Catalysis Research Center. His main research topics are similar to mine. He has concentrated on hydrogen electrode reactions. His department head was Michio Enyo, who subsequently retired and became the dean of The Hakodate School of Engineering. Enyo has been engaged in cold fusion research from the beginning. He was the one who suggested that Ohmori take up the research, back in 1989. Ohmori began with an utterly negative attitude, but when he did the experiments he observed anomalous heat, and this completely changed his point of view. However, the heat was so small and the results varied so widely, he felt that at this rate the research would wither away, and he wanted to do something to make it more robust. One day, after using a glass cell to electrolyze gold in light water, he noticed that many black dirt particles had collected at the bottom of the cell. When he saw that, Ohmori felt disappointed that he had let in so much contamination.

Actually, it was not contamination. He set to work analyzing the dirt to find out where and how it had entered the cell. He examined the particles with his own Auger electron spectroscope (AES), and to his astonishment he discovered they were iron. Before the experiment, in the preparation phase, iron was nowhere to be found. Why was there so much of it afterward? The water, electrode, and cell he used were made of high purity materials. Only one explanation seemed to fit the facts: the iron must have appeared as the product of some kind of reaction. What if this was a nuclear reaction? The isotopic distribution might be affected. In that case, Ohmori reasoned, there ought to be heat and other products. He set to work at once performing a mass spec analysis, and when he computed the results he was struck dumb with amazement. The isotopic distribution was extraordinary. Natural iron has four isotopes:

Mass Number	Percent of Sample
54	5.8%
56	91.72%
57	2.2%
58	0.28%

These percentages are the same in all naturally occurring samples, not varying by even 0.1%. But Ohmori's sample was completely different. At the surface, just over half the metal was iron-57, which is usually only 2%, and 45% was iron-56 (usually 92%). Below the surface the distribution gradually reverted closer to normal, but at 3,000 angstroms iron-57 still constituted 15% of the metal, and iron-56 was only 80%. There were practically no other elements in the sample, so the influence of peaks from other elements and compounds like iron oxide was not a factor.

However many times he repeated the experiment, Ohmori always observed iron, and every time the isotopes were unnatural. He deliberately added iron to the solution before electrolysis. The iron that appeared on the surface had perfectly natural isotopic abundances. He determined that the strange abundances only began to appear after seven days of electrolysis with a treated cathode surface, purified water, and high current density.

Ohmori prepared a report on his findings and tried to publish it, but nobody would deal with him. It was then that the conference in Texas was held. Here, where many of the presenters reported on various anomalous changes to the nucleus, Ohmori's data attracted the most attention because of its precision and good reproducibility.

After consulting with Oriani we left Minnesota and headed for San Francisco. Our objective was SRI International at Stanford University. This was where an accident had occurred during a cold fusion experiment, but McKubre and three other researchers did not lose heart; they continued to work vigorously. I had visited SRI previously, on December 11, 1993, but unfortunately I did not have a chance to see McKubre on that occasion. Azumi, a former Hokkaido student, had given me a tour of the facility on that previous trip, so I knew my way around. The bright California sunlight in June made it a hot summer.

When I went into the beautiful SRI laboratories, the contrast to my own laboratory was so great I felt disoriented, as if I had stumbled into a different world. They have ten rooms, with dozens of working cells, and data collection is fully computerized and automatic. The rooms themselves are held at a constant temperature, and within the rooms are special chambers held at even more stringent temperature levels. Many cells were set up.

After we toured the lab, we presented our own results. McKubre and the others were quite interested in hearing what we had to say, but their questions were mainly about the correlation of heat and evolved elements. Something McKubre said when we parted left a strong impression on me: "I, too, am very interested in nuclear products. But our sponsor intends to put heat first, so we must make it the centerpiece of our program. That is why I am trying to increase deuterium loading." I could not accept this way of thinking. I understand why he wants heat. And surely the more deuterons you load in a lattice, the smaller the gap between deuterons will be. But no matter how high you make it, deuteron density will be many orders of magnitude too low for a spontaneous reaction to occur. Right from the start there was no way you could explain this purely in terms of a D-D reaction. By this time I was beginning to think it must be something completely different.

After I got home from Texas, I started a serious, full-scale analysis of nuclear products. In my department we have a scanning electron microscope with an EDX spectrograph built in. Of course it is an old thing, 20 years out of date. The control program loads off floppy diskettes—eight-inch diskettes at that. I repaired the high voltage circuits and the pre-amp power supply, and calibrated at different energy levels. By the time I got everything working it was November 1995.

On November 27, I took a proton conductor which had undergone a sharp temperature rise—I had not been able to measure exactly how much heat, but it partially melted—and I analyzed the area around the melted crater with the EDX. Naturally, the elements the conductor was made of showed up: strontium, cerium, platinum. Aside from these, distinct peaks for iron, copper and lead appeared. No trace of elements like iron were supposed to exist in the sample, the sample holder, or gas. I thought it was strange, so I quickly had a look at a reserved, unused sample, and I analyzed the other cell materials one by one: the cylinder, the raw materials for the conductors, the thermocouples, the platinum electrodes. I soon realized that elements like iron were only found in samples that had undergone anomalous melting and bursts of excess heat, and all such samples had these elements. The reaction was localized, and the total density of these elements could only be estimated. I became intensely curious about the palladium, nickel, gold and platinum cathodes we had used in experiments over the years. I quickly contacted Ohmori to discuss his results in detail. He had mainly reported results with iron, investigating the isotopic distribution with mass spectroscopy.

I decided to analyze the cathodes from my experiments with palladium alloys. (I had continued doing these experiments while I explored other materials.) On January 7, 1996, when I still felt in a New Year's holiday mood, I investigated the palladium and discovered a fabulous array of unexpected elements in large amounts: silicon, calcium, titanium, chromium, iron, manganese, cobalt, nickel, copper, zinc, platinum, lead, and more. In Ohmori's cathodes I detected significant amounts of iron, copper, nickel, platinum, osmium, mercury and lead.

We asked an outside laboratory to perform an independent analysis of the palladium. The results came back to us on the morning of February 14. Ohmori, who rarely becomes excited, called me in a tizzy. *

"Mizuno, the results are back. It's incredible! All kinds of elements have come out: iron, copper, chromium, platinum, lithium, titanium, cadmium, there's more and more. And the isotopic distribution is completely out of whack. I've never seen anything like it. There is no copper-65. There's only one peak for copper, at mass 63. Anyway, I'll be right over."

In less than five minutes Ohmori showed up, puffing and panting, carrying a thick stack of data sheets. As he spread them out, he said, "Look at these numbers!" pointing to ten sheets of graphs. They showed results for various elements: boron, potassium, titanium, chrome, copper, zinc, bromine, palladium, cadmium, xenon, hafnium, rhenium, osmium, iridium, platinum, mercury, and lead. "To start with, I computed the results for these. There are more, but the clearest data is from these. The isotope distribution for every one of them is shifted. Especially chrome and copper are incredibly anomalous," he said, riffling through the pages as he showed me the data. There were many graphs in an easily understood format, showing for each element the natural isotopic distribution and the analyzed distribution, in solid and dotted lines. The two lines did not overlap in a single case.

"This is astounding," I said. "The samples from before electrolysis show no isotope shifts in the contamination, and not much contamination at that. As you go deeper down the isotope shifts fade out, and you get back to the natural isotopes. Why should that be? Look: the changes at the surface seem to be larger. Do you think we are seeing overlaid peaks from other elements?"

"No fear," he replied. "The ones where that might be a problem are not included. For example, argon or neon will overlap with various oxides, so they are excluded."

"How about the sensitivity correction? They are measuring this with oxygen ions, right? In that case the alkalies will be way more sensitive, won't they? It seems to me compared to the noble gases they will be six orders of magnitude greater."

"That's right. With the ones you hit with oxygen, carbides are a problem. Use cesium, and the carbonates mask out everything else."

"It sounds like a lot of bother," I remarked. "Let's look at data from another location, and from another sample."

---

*Hitachi provided 220 peaks on 500 pages of data. Ultimately four independent analyses on the cathode materials were performed by: Techno Research Laboratory, Hitachi Instruments Engineering Co., Ltd., Hitachinaka City; Nissan Analysis and Research Center at Yokosuka City; Mitsubishi Heavy Industry Co. at Nagasaki City; Meidenshya Co.

"It has all been computed already. Here is a sample that produced no heat. Generally speaking the shifts are not big. But you note there are many heavy elements. And here is another piece from the same sample, which did produce heat. The distribution of elements is similar, and the distribution of isotopes is the same."

"Still—all in all—this is astounding data. Do you think the instrument is working right?"

"No problem. Plenty of the samples show nothing. The calibration is all right. They ran a variety of elements and alloys, and samples from before electrolysis."

"I understand. Let us wait until we receive other analyses before we reach the final conclusion," I said, wrapping up the conversation.

Immediately after that I sent the same materials to two other independent laboratories for analysis. It was a blind test: I mixed in samples of ordinary material as a control, without telling the laboratories which materials had undergone electrolysis. The anomalies were confirmed. The results showed that the distribution of elements and isotope shifts varied from place to place on the surface in the bulk of the sample, suggesting the kinds of variations in the electrochemical reaction that may be responsible. I wanted a precise distribution analysis. I asked Kurokawa and another independent lab for an EPMA analysis. I myself continued to perform EDX analyses every day, to determine the density of elements. With Kitaichi's help I was able to transfer the EDX data into a computer for additional processing, making the results extremely accurate. My own computer system was upgraded at this time, which led to big changes in my research methodology. To make a long story short, I got access to the Internet, which gave me the ability to exchange messages with researchers worldwide.

Bockris, Tom Passell, Hal Fox, Ben Bush* and others sent message after message with exciting news. Other researchers sent raw data, saying that they too had observed changes in isotopes. They realized that these changes were similar to the shifts in palladium that I had reported earlier.

I immediately wrote up my results in a paper which I submitted to a number of journals. The submissions I sent overseas came back before long with referee comments turning them down. The reasons given were: 1) Nuclear changes caused by chemical reactions cannot be accepted; 2) There is no theoretical explanation in the paper; 3) The writing and grammar were poor. I rewrote the paper and sent it again, but it was again rejected. In response to journals that had said there was no theoretical explanation, I wrote a the-

---

* Dr. Benjamin F. Bush, University of Texas, Austin, Texas

ory, adding the proviso that it was strictly deductive (derived from data). They responded by rejecting the paper because the theory was too strange. In short, the policy was that no paper about cold fusion would be accepted under any circumstances, as I well understood.

While I was going back and forth with these submissions, I received a message from George Miley, editor of the journal *Fusion Technology*. It astonished me. It was about a paper describing experiments that he himself had done with nickel coated beads in light water, in which 40% of the cathode metal changed to some other element.* He is the head of an enterprising research team at the University of Illinois which is developing the Patterson Power Cell** into a practical kit to allow the detection of cold fusion. The reaction cell does not employ an ordinary cathode, but rather glass beads covered with a thin film of nickel. The data from post-electrolysis cathodes was remarkably similar to the data from my used palladium cathodes. My work was finally being recognized by American researchers.[9]

When American researchers judge they might be able to make something worthwhile, they immediately take steps to get a patent. Of course, cold fusion devices are no exception. Many patent applications have already been made, and in fact a few have been granted. The basic idea or materials, the method, or the machine itself are prime targets for patents. In this regard Japan is clearly behind the times. I have some misgivings, wondering if America might monopolize cold fusion energy.

The Patterson Power Cell is based on old ideas. The initial patent was granted by the U.S. Patent Office on January 4, 1972 and assigned number 3,632,496. The glass beads used as cathode material are also covered by a patent, number 4,943,355, issued July 24, 1990. An improvement to that was granted June 30, 1991, number 5,036,031. The reactor itself was covered on June 7 and December 13, 1994, in patents 5,318,675 and 5,372,688. Of course the device itself may not even work as far as I know, but I think we can learn a lesson from the Americans about the importance of moving quickly.

In March 1996 I not only submitted a paper about the isotopic distribution anomalies to overseas journals, but also to Japanese electrochemical journals. The judgements from two referees differed. One said that if I added detailed information about experimental conditions it would be okay. The

---

*Electrolysis with nickel beads . . . after thirteen days of electrolysis in a 1-molar lithium sulfate solution, many anomalous isotopes are observed on the thin film metal surface, especially iron, copper, magnesium, and chromium.
**Patterson Power Cell was developed at CETI, Clean Energy Technologies, Inc., now located in Sarasota, Florida. Both the beads and the cell design were patented in 1994. See U.S. patents 5,372,688, 5,318,675.

other referee said that my paper overturned established scientific principles, so before he judged it he wanted me to provide more details on reproducibility, contamination, and so on. I immediately rewrote and resubmitted it. I soon received a communication saying the paper was accepted. It was April 4, 1996.[10]

Second International Low Energy Nuclear Reactions Conference (ILENR-2)

In April 1996 Bockris sent me a letter announcing the second ILENR conference. It was to be in September because he wanted to hold it just before the Sixth International Conference on Cold Fusion (ICCF-6) in October. I had a lot to talk about this time; I responded that I would be delighted to attend. After a while another letter from Bockris came, saying that the conference would not be held at the university, but at a hotel nearby. When he applied for space at the university, Bockris was told by a chemistry department committee that "cold fusion does not exist," ergo this theme is a "joke" and a meeting room cannot be made available for it. The conference was obstructed for this preposterous reason. In an incident during the previous conference a participant had been assaulted by a chemistry department faculty member. To think that such dastardly acts should take place in an academic setting—in freedom-loving America, no less!

At the risk of repeating myself, I must point out that a clear conclusion has yet to emerge from this field. It was the U.S. Department of Energy which simply dismissed cold fusion after a mere six months of experiments done by who-knows-who, producing unclear results. Thanks to that fiasco, researchers in this field all over the world have been the targets of unfounded, unreasonable discrimination and censure.

On September 11, 1996, I departed for Texas. I arrived in San Francisco ten hours after leaving Osaka airport. The flight we held reservations for had left an hour late, so we missed the connection to Dallas. We had an hour transit time at San Francisco, but only 25 minutes at Dallas. I must say though, San Francisco looked green and inviting. I visited this town for the first time in March 1985 on my way back from Texas to Japan, and I was moved by its beauty. In December 1993 after ICCF-4 I visited it again, and this time I was disappointed by the trashy, run-down appearance of things. In June 1995 I saw it again from inside a taxi after a major earthquake, and I was astounded by the sight. I get a different impression of the city every time I come. This time I had to rush through. The layover at Dallas was also brief, leaving only ten minutes to rush to another terminal by shuttle. By the time I finally got aboard the small commuter airplane bound for College Station, it was 8:30 p.m.

I was soon flying through the pitch-dark Texas sky. The only proof that the land was inhabited were a few lights from towns on the band of the horizon, and the headlights of cars on the highways. In only ten years I have been drawn here three times; my fate must be tied to Texas, somehow.

I arrived in College Station at 9:45. A few days before I left Japan, Bockris faxed saying I would be met at the airport. I was surprised to see Bockris himself waiting for me. I guess he was looking forward to our meeting as much as I was. On the way to the hotel we got a chance to talk for the first time in a long time. He was hard at work as keenly as ever, but the hardships were also continuing as ever. The number of post-doctoral students in his lab had declined to four or five people, only a fifth of what it had been at its peak.

Bockris said he would retire next year (1997). The inevitable has finally come to pass, I thought grimly. From now on, cold fusion will have to make progress without Bockris. In Japan too, Norio Sato, Michio Enyo, Hideo Ikegami and other leading researchers have all gone. When the leading researchers leave one after another, I fear for what will become of the field.

The meeting was held for two days starting September 13, at a Holiday Inn hotel. The main theme was that products are generated in the cathode from the action of electrolysis and other methods of loading. The evidence for this was clearer than it had been in the previous conference. The first presentation was by George Miley, who began speaking in a quiet, calm tone; at first glance it was almost as if he lacked self-confidence. I already knew the content of his report, but hearing the details of the experiment and measurement techniques directly from the man himself gave it a completely new meaning. There is something good about meeting in person; it gives you a feel for the value of the work as well as the man. In recent years improvements to the Internet have greatly speeded up the exchange of information, but when you meet people in the flesh, you realize that the Internet is no substitute for first-hand human contact.

My presentation came after Miley's, and as usual I read from a prepared manuscript. Try as I might, I cannot ad lib a presentation in English. If I get hung up for even a second, I lose track of what I mean to say. My mind goes blank, because I am thinking in one language and expressing myself in another, and the transition back and forth is difficult. When I finished the presentation, the question and answer period began. Unlike the previous conference, the questions were about rather mundane, basic topics, like the distribution and depth of the shifted isotopes, and the amount of contamination. There were no penetrating questions expressing doubt about these surprising results. I found this something of a let down.

There were 21 presentations in all, most of them describing the results of analysis for reaction products, or theories. The truth is, I felt uneasy because few people questioned whether transmutation really did occur. The results were taken for granted, as if they were an expected, natural extension to earlier cold fusion findings. In some of the talks the measurement conditions were not clear, or the treatments to exclude contamination were not described adequately, which made me feel doubtful. Especially when there are only tiny quantities of products, contamination that adheres to the cathode during electrolysis (material galvanized onto the cathode) becomes a severe problem. I cannot accept assertions that such material must be the product of transmutation. If some sort of reaction is occurring, I take it for granted that the distribution of isotopes has to be different from the natural distribution, and it is reasonable to assume that radioactive elements will also be produced. At this conference there were a few reports of production of radioactive elements, but they were notable mainly for their poor reproducibility. People who reported on shifts in the distribution of isotopes included Miley, Bockris, Ohmori and myself. In these cases, accurate investigations employed EDX, EPMA, SIMS and several methods of detecting radioactive substances. (See glossary.) This kind of research is extremely laborious and complex, making it hard to convince other people of the results.

With 21 presentations and 40 attendees, the conference was about the same as the previous year. However, except for a few papers that reached vague conclusions, the content of the many presentations was improved and more accurate, giving a sense of sure and steady progress. The open forum discussion period at the end of the conference touched on experiments in many parts of the world, and many participants were particularly interested in hearing about research in Japan. For several years little real progress has been seen in this field. But this conference was more positive, and replete with new developments.

The Sixth International Conference on Cold Fusion

Soon after the meeting in Texas ended and I returned home, the Sixth International Conference (ICCF-6) began. It was held over a six-day period, from October 13 - 18, in Hokkaido in the mountain top resort Apex Hotel next to Lake Toya. I had invited Dr. and Mrs. Oriani from Minnesota to visit Sapporo for a week before the conference. He had confirmed excess heat with the proton conductors I sent, and he was going to present his results at the conference. Our purpose was to discuss detailed arrangements and my own continuing replications.

His experimental technique was flawless. His measurement technique was like flow calorimetry in that it showed absolute heat, leaving little chance of error. To perfect it even more, Oriani had sent back to Sapporo a mixed selection of used conductor samples, some which had produced heat in Oriani's lab, and some which had not. He sent along instructions asking me to run them again in my own calorimeter. In short, it was a blind test in which I did not know which samples had previously produced heat.*

I had set about making the measurements from the first of the year, and I gathered data for about a month. The results were that two samples produced heat, and the others produced none. I sent these results back to Oriani. Of those two samples, one did not produce any heat at Oriani's place, but the other one definitely did. As a result of additional analysis, in the samples that worked we found potassium, calcium, iron, lead, titanium and so on. But, the ever-cautious Oriani was not satisfied with these results. As for me, I thought that the irreproducibility was a function of complex reactions on the surface and interface, and that results would change with treatment methods and the conditions under which the temperature was measured. Oriani was also not satisfied with the detection of elements in the sample that had produced heat in both labs. I invited him so that we could perform the final check together.

On October 8, past nine in the evening, I waited in the airport lobby for the Orianis to arrive on the last incoming flight. A few figures were scattered around the dimly lit terminal. A few sat in the arrival lobby waiting area, waiting for the flight from Osaka. The sign indicated it would be delayed fifteen minutes, but it came in a few minutes later. A dozen passengers hurried off into the night, and then the Orianis appeared, walking down the staircase at a leisurely pace. I waved and they soon caught sight of me, and waved back, smiling with apparent relief.

They said it had been a long trip but they were fine now. In the car Oriani talked about his impressions of Japan, and asked me rapid-fire questions about the experiment. We went along the freeway, into the city to a hotel near the university. Oriani likes Japan. For years he hosted Japanese researchers when they visited the University of Minnesota. Many people, starting with Norio Sato, eagerly awaited Oriani's return visit to our university.

Come to think of it, researchers from around the world have visited my

*Oriani uses a Seebeck envelope calorimeter. This type captures and accounts for virtually all of the heat, rather than sampling the temperature at one spot.]

laboratory by now. First Srinivasan from India, then Celani and Scaramuzzi from Italy;* from America McKubre, Passell and Bush; from Japan, Hideo Ikegami, Eichi Yamaguchi, Akito Takahashi, and a crowd of others have come.

These researchers form the group that has sustained cold fusion. They have been treated like heretics by the rest of the scientific community. This has formed what should be called a bond of solidarity between them. These researchers, working with practically no funding, have continued experiments against a powerful tide of opposition. By their intense efforts, they have gradually, slowly but surely brought about a new discovery. The bonds I have formed with these people are extremely precious to me and I would not exchange them for anything. Naturally, there are many other magnificent researchers besides the people I noted above. It would be impossible to list them all here. The important point is that one researcher working alone cannot make progress in science.

I met with Oriani several times to discuss the experiments and resolve some disagreements and confusion. The day before the conference opened, we finally reached a consensus. We ascertained the main discrepancy was a mere misunderstanding; I had mislabeled one of the drawings I sent to Oriani.

It turned out Oriani had long been interested in reaction products. I finally got him to talk about this aspect of his work. Around 1992, Oriani used a SIMS to investigate a cathode that had produced excess heat. He said he found that isotopes on the surface were significantly shifted from natural abundances. To be specific, Pd-104 and Pd-105 were reduced; Pd-106 and Pd-110 were increased. This is not what I usually found. My results showed Pd-104 and Pd-102 increased, and Pd-106 and Pd-108 reduced. Oriani's results were similar to what I saw with samples that did not produce significant heat. Oriani's electrolyte was D_2O-Li_2SO_4, whereas I used D_2O- LiOD. Because of these differences we could not report his palladium results compared to mine, and it was impossible to further analyze his results because he had not preserved the sample.

Thus, the Sixth International Conference began. One hundred eighty people from seventeen countries participated, one hundred twenty presentations were made. Highlighting this conference were seven papers on transmutation. Aside from these, transmutation data was shown in several other oral presentations. In particular, the existence of transmutation was strongly

*Dr. Francesco Celani, INFN, Frascati, Italy;
 Dr. Francesco Scaramuzzi, ENEA, Frascati, Italy

suggested in presentations by Russian scientists Karabut, Savvatimova and Samgin.* The main focus of the conference was, as usual, excess heat, and I got the impression that other subjects were being swept under the carpet. My own report was relegated to a poster session, so I was not able to talk to many people about it, regrettably. Even at that, I got a chance to discuss it with Mallove, Hora,** Storms and many others, which is a pretty good catch for a poster session.

As soon as the conference ended I met with Hora and Miley to discuss the experiments in detail. We agreed that the most important consideration is dealing with impurities: how to exclude them as much as possible, and how to account for the effects of those remaining. We also discussed the changes in isotope distribution, and the origin of light elements in my experiment. To summarize, we made the point I have been emphasizing for a long time: it is not necessarily the case that heat production means a reaction, and no heat means no reaction. There may be endothermic reactions that absorb heat instead of producing it. This is an important clue to understanding the reaction mechanism. In many experiments until now, samples that did not produce heat were put aside and not analyzed. I believe important data may well have been overlooked when these samples were ignored.

*Dr. Alexander B. Karabut, Lubertsl, Moscow Region, Russia; Dr. Irina B. Savvatimova, Scientific Industrial Association "LUTCH" Research Institute, Podolsk, Moscow Region, Russia; Dr. Alexander L. Samgin, Institute of High-Temperature Electrochemistry, Ekaterinburg, Russia

**Prof. Heinrich Hora, Department of Theoretical Physics, University of New South Wales, Sydney, Australia; Dr. Eugene Mallove, engineer and *Infinite Energy* editor

7

WHAT IS THE COLD FUSION REACTION?

Reaction Products and the Mechanism that Generates Them

After ICCF-6, as 1996 was drawing to a close, I received an e-mail message. It was from the Italian physicist E. Conte. He had seen a report on the transmutation products generated in my cell, and he wanted detailed information about other nuclear products like neutrons and charged particles. He said he had a theory that could explain cold fusion.[11]

Up until now many theories to explain the mechanism of cold fusion have been proposed, but they have been inadequate. First came the ordinary D-D reaction hypothesis, then cracking (fractofusion), muon catalyzed, multibody, and neutron catalyzed fusion hypotheses. With each of them it was difficult to thoroughly explain all aspects of the phenomenon. Each of these hypotheses addressed a different aspect of the problem in an *ad hoc* fashion. Compared to the others up until now, Conte's theory is both simpler and more powerful because, by introducing a simple extension of the conventional quantum mechanical wave function, the theory accounts for all observed effects directly from first principles.

Many people upon hearing "quantum mechanics" will assume his theory is filled with a tangle of equations and abstruse physics, and reject it for that reason alone. But a quantum mechanical field is nothing special. It is a logical theory that fits the experimental evidence, and it did not spring out of nowhere. It is built upon classical physics. Just as a new house cannot be built with only old materials, so the new theory incorporates new extensions to existing theory. One of these is the idea of one-body particle waves. By "particles," we mean the subatomic constituents of ordinary matter, such as electrons or protons. "Waves" refer to energy fluctuations. In the past, these were considered completely separate things. A wave could not become a particle or vice versa. Without doubt that holds true for the phenomena we can observe directly. But when you enter the world of matter too small to be seen with the human eye, like atoms, molecules, subatomic particles, the situation is completely different. At this level, matter can behave as either a particle, or a wave, and sometimes as both simultaneously.

Therefore, we may ask: Is the world of visible, macroscopic matter governed by the classical laws of mechanics, while quantum mechanics is limited to a small set of specialized, microscopic reactions? No, that is not how it works. Quantum mechanics applies to all matter, including everything we can see, but the quantum effects are usually too small to be perceived directly. Using classical mechanics we can explain the visible effects of quantum mechanics to a close approximation.

In 1923 de Broglie had a bold idea. He predicted that particles (such as electrons) would have certain wave-like properties. This was quickly verified by the electron diffraction experiments of Davisson and Germer.

Consider energy. The concept of energy is the bridge from classical mechanics to quantum theory. The total energy of any system is defined as the sum of its kinetic and potential energy:

$$E \text{ (energy)} = mv^2/2 \text{ (kinetic energy)} + V \text{ (potential energy)} \quad (1)$$

In classical mechanics, a single particle of mass m moving at velocity v has kinetic energy $T = mv^2/2$, or in terms of the particle's momentum p (defined by $p = mv$), $T = p^2/2\ m$. If the particle is moving under the influence of an externally applied potential V, we have:

$$E = p^2/2\ m + V \quad (2)$$

Now from Einstein's photoelectric theory, it is known that a beam of monochromatic light can be thought of as a stream of particles, called "photons," each of which carries energy E expressed as:

$$E = h\nu \quad (3)$$

Here, h is Planck's constant, 6.63×10^{-34} joule-seconds, and ν is the light's frequency (cycles/second). From this, we see that a photon's energy is proportional to its frequency.

De Broglie's idea, radical at the time, was simply this: To endow a particle of mass m with wave-like characteristics, the energy of the particle (according to Eq. 2) must equal the energy in the wave (according to Eq. 3). In other words,

$$h\nu = p^2/2m + V \quad (4)$$

De Broglie then rearranged Einstein's equation $E = mc^2$ to obtain $m = E/c^2$, and set $E = h\nu$ (per Eq. 3), and assumed velocity v = c (speed of light). Substituting all this into the classical definition of momentum, he wrote:

$$p = mv = hv/c = h/\lambda = hk \tag{5}$$

where λ = wavelength, and k = $1/\lambda$ = wave-number. Finally, substituting p from Eq. 5 into Eq. 2 yields the important result:

$$hv = h^2k^2/2m + V \tag{6}$$

Eq. 6 expresses the concept that particles and waves are different aspects of the same thing. That being the case, consider how to represent a wave. The most familiar method is to use circular functions (sine and cosine). Using the Greek letter ψ to represent instantaneous wave amplitude, the formula looks like this:

$$\psi = r \sin \theta \quad \text{or} \quad \psi = r \cos \theta \tag{7}$$

Here, r has the units of amplitude, θ is the spin angle. In a one dimensional representation, we assume that the wave amplitude ψ is a function of position (x) and time (t):

$$\psi(x,t) = r \sin \theta (x, t) \quad \text{or} \quad \psi (x, t) = r \cos \theta (x, t) \tag{8}$$

Also, we will write the phase angle θ as a function of x and t as follows:
$$\theta (x,t) = 2 \pi n (x, t) = 2 \pi (kx-\gamma t)$$
$$\psi = r \sin 2\pi n(x, t) \quad \text{or} \quad \psi = r \cos 2\pi n(x, t) \tag{9}$$

Since it is a nuisance to distinguish between sin and cos, Euler's formula ($e^{i\theta} = \cos \theta + i \sin \theta$) can be used to express equations 8 and 9 more elegantly, as follows:
$$\psi = r e^{\, i2\pi \, (kx-\gamma t)} \tag{10}$$

With this, the de Broglie formula (eq. 6) becomes:

$$- (1 / i2\pi) \; \partial \psi / \partial t = (-h^2 / 8\pi^2 m) \; \partial^2 \psi / \partial x^2 + V\psi \tag{11}$$

This is the basic formula of quantum mechanics, known as Schrödinger's equation. The symbol ψ (called the wavefunction) represents the wave which corresponds to the particle of matter. By solving this equation for specified boundary conditions and applied potentials, the particle's behavior can be predicted, at least in principle.

But solving Schrödinger's equation is usually not easy. To start with, two critical parameters—the type of particle, and its potential energy V—must be known. In other words, one must specify the particle's potential state, in order to solve the equation. Even for a simple particle like a hydrogen atom, the computation is quite involved. For more complicated systems, a closed-form solution is usually impossible unless several approximations are made.

In Eq. 11, the time derivative $(\partial\psi/\partial t)$ is multiplied by the imaginary unit i. To remove the resulting complex-valued factors, it is necessary to convert it to a stationary state equation (eliminating time as a factor). The result is called the Schrödinger stationary state equation:

$$E\psi = (-h^2/8\pi^2 m)\,(\partial^2\psi/\partial x^2) + V\,\psi \tag{12}$$

To solve this, one must consider the potential energy V of all interactions that are present (*e.g.,* electromagnetic waves, magnetic forces, spin, etc.).

For example, the solution for a hydrogen atom (one electron in orbit around one proton) is fairly straightforward, and it produces a value reasonably close to the actual measured one. With a hydrogen molecule (two protons and two electrons), there are more interactions to be accounted for, and the solution is quite complicated.

What Conte decided at this stage was to grapple directly with the problem of interactions between electrons and the nucleus, which are usually ignored. In general, the potential at distance r from a nucleus of positive charge Z can be represented as follows:

$$V = -Ze^2/4\pi\varepsilon_0 r \tag{13}$$

where ε_0 = dielectric permittivity of free space.

However, in addition to this, over very short distances another term works:

$$V' = -k\exp(-ar)/[1-\exp(-ar)] \tag{14}$$

According to this equation, a strong interaction occurs between electrons and hydrogen atoms when placed in conditions of extreme high temperature and pressure, or electrolysis at very high current density. In the liquid in a cell are many ions that make it an electrolyte; for example, Li, Na and K ions are usually present. Under powerful electrolysis, these ions are galvanized onto the surface of the cathode, and it is well known that they have a major influence on the electrolysis process. When a discharge reaction (defined in detail below) causes the ions in the liquid, including these alkali metal ions, to have strong interactions, it may give rise to the potential shown in equation 14. In this case, the area affected by the electrolytic potential is very small. Therefore, by Heisenberg's principle, the uncertainty in the momentum it imparts to ions and electrons becomes very large. Since position and momentum are a conjugate pair of variables, decreasing the uncertainty of one member of this pair increases the uncertainty of its conjugate partner. For instance, if an electrolytic potential is localized to extremely small areas on the cathode, the uncertainty in the momentum it imparts to ions and electrons in solution could become very large. In this case, it may be possible for some of these electrons to acquire sufficient energy to tunnel into the nucleus. As a result, electron capture occurs, inside the hydrogen atoms and alkaline metal atoms, the electrons combine with protons to form neutrons.

One natural form of this type of electron capture is known to occur, in which heavy elements are made stable. This is a form of radioactive decay in which one proton from inside the nucleus captures one electron from an orbit of the same atom to form a neutron, while at the same time releasing a neutron from the nucleus. The same kind of interaction occurs during beta decay. Depending on the orbit the captured electron occupied, this is called K shell capture, L shell capture, or M shell capture.

This reaction can also be caused by accelerating an electron outside of the atom and impacting it onto the atom with such force that it penetrates to the nucleus and combines with a proton. This process requires extremely high energy levels. It has been demonstrated with a powerful linear accelerator at Stanford University operating at 30 billion volts. At these extreme power levels the reaction occurs easily, but the energy release is so large, the proton is transformed into a variety of particles.

In this case the potential of the entire system acts as a powerful force between electron and proton. In other words, the entire potential is $V + V'$. With these interactive effects, the following reaction between the proton and the electron occurs, and as a result a neutron is produced:

$$p + e^- \rightarrow n + \text{neutrinos} \tag{15}$$

When this is not a proton but a deuteron, you get this reaction:

$$d + e^- \rightarrow 2n + \text{neutrinos} \tag{16}$$

Compared to many other reactions that have been proposed, this one is markedly better at explaining the observed experimental results. The sporadic production of neutrons, the tritium production at orders of magnitude higher than neutrons, the sudden onset of heat, the dearth of radioactivity, the difference between hydrogen and heavy hydrogen, and finally the anomalous isotope reaction products can all be explained by this. This theory is most effective at explaining the difference between electrolysis with light and heavy hydrogen, and the reaction products from each. The hydrogen electrolysis reaction produces neutrons, which go into the nuclei of the cathode metal atoms, producing heavier elements. When these are unstable, they undergo beta decay to become more stable elements. Depending on how the neutrons enter the nuclei the elements do not always convert to heavier elements, but in some cases nuclear fission occurs until a stable isotope is formed. In this case, a large mass deficit is created, causing huge amounts of heat.

What Is a Hydrogen Cathode Reaction?

Here is the important question: Is there really an interactive effect between electrons and protons during an electrolytic hydrogen production reaction? If we can clarify these conditions, it follows that the other reactions described by Conte must occur.

When an accelerator is used to strike a nucleus with an electron at giga-electron volt orders of energy, it enters the nucleus easily, and breaks it into pieces, but is it possible to derive such enormous power from electrolysis? Normally the answer is no, it would be impossible. But that response does not get us anywhere. What is the actual condition of the hydrogen nucleus and electron during electrolysis? Unfortunately, at present this is not well understood.

Seen on the atomic level, the metal surface is a collection of crystals (grains), with many defects, contaminants, oxides, and so on, having complex physical properties. Depending on whether the electrolyte is acidic, neutral or alkaline, the reaction takes place in different ways, but in macroscopic terms it can be explained as follows. When the metal is placed in a solution and positively charged, hydrogen $H+$ ions approach the metal surface. They bond with electrons, becoming hydrogen atoms, and then they are absorbed by the metal surface. This is called the discharge reaction, and it requires a certain level of activation energy. This energy is called "discharge overpotential."

After hydrogen atoms are absorbed by the surface, they unite in pairs to form hydrogen molecules, which leave the metal surface as hydrogen gas. The energy required at this stage is called "recombination overpotential" and it can be directly computed as the pressure from hydrogen formation. If overpotential is zero at this time, hydrogen forms with exactly one atmosphere of pressure. If overpotential is 30 millivolts, the pressure is 10 atmospheres. At 60 millivolts it goes to 100 atmospheres; at 150 millivolts it reaches a hundred thousand atmospheres, increasing logarithmically—according to Enyo's theory, which has been confirmed by experiment. We know that this overpotential is changed by current density, the condition of the electrolyte, and the state of the metal surface. Among these, current density usually has a logarithmic effect. With palladium in a 1 molar LiOD solution, when current density is 10 milliamps per square centimeter, overpotential is 0.3 volts. When current density is 100 milliamps per square centimeter, overpotential is 0.9 volts; overpotential equals current density raised to the one-fourth power.

Looking at it this way, you can compute that pressure increases by the fourth power compared to overpotential, and in the end the power density and pressure are mostly proportional. One milliamp produces 700 atmospheres, 10 milliamps produces 5,500 atmospheres, and 100 milliamps, it turns out, produce 50,000 atmospheres. That being the case, you might suppose you can increase pressure indefinitely by increasing the electric current, but things do not work out so easily.

When this research got underway, Fleischmann and Pons did not understand the hydrogen electrolysis reaction in enough detail, and I think they made a major error in their paper. They claimed that when electrolysis current density reaches 0.6 amperes per square centimeter, overpotential reaches 1.5 volts. Therefore, since $1400/30 = 46.7$, pressure as high as 10^{47} atmospheres can be achieved, which should suffice to cause nuclear fusion. However, that is not the case. What they call "overpotential" includes both the electrical discharge reaction and the recombination (D_2 formation) reaction. But pressure is a function of recombination overpotential alone. Enyo's experiments revealed that no matter how much you increase the current, recombination overpotential will not exceed ~150 millivolts, in which case pressure is $150/30 = 5$, in other words, it reaches only about 10^5 atmospheres.[12]

Many researchers assume that if they can cram a large quantity of deuterons into palladium, it ought to generate heat. They think there must be a connection between loading and heat, so they place considerable emphasis on this goal. But, however much you increase current density, that alone can never increase deuteron loading (the D/Pd ratio) beyond unity. You can heat up the lattice or expose it to a magnetic field; you can anneal the palladium, or alloy it to other metals. You can process the metal to make the surface smooth. Nothing will help.

Does that leave no way to produce heat? What sort of reaction is cold fusion? Could it be D-D fusion? As you have seen in this account so far, we still have no clear idea what it is. It might even be something that nobody has even dreamed of yet. Let us consider that possibility.

Condition of the Metal Surface After Use as a Cathode

In November 1995, we investigated Ohmori's gold cathodes using a scanning electron microscope. At a low magnification of 100x, we saw the surface was sprinkled with white spots. When we magnified one of these white spots, we were astounded. At 2000x we saw several objects shaped like lilies (see Figure 8) stretched in a line. We magnified it further, and saw that the objects had a fibrous, lace-like structure. At the center of the structure was a deep hole, like a caldera, and near the edge of it many six-sided crystals lay on top of one another. In the heart of the structure the round hole led into the metal, with the surrounding material projecting out across the rim of the opening. The lilies had only appeared in areas that had been heavily processed by scraping with quartz glass before electrolysis. There was no trace of them in other areas.

Exactly the same thing had happened to the palladium electrolyzed in heavy water. Especially large numbers of lilies formed in samples that had been electrolyzed repeatedly. The thick bar of palladium had so many of them, the entire bar looked black to the naked eye. Based on this, it was clear that the reaction was not taking place inside the palladium (in the bulk) but

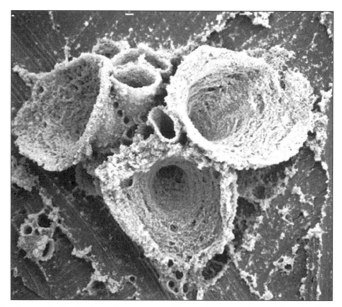

Figure 8. Products found on the surface of Ohmori's gold cathode after electrolysis. Lilly shaped eduction that forms when a pure gold foil was heavily electrolyzed in Na_2CO_3 (sodium carbonate). The diameter of the objects is 10 μm, height about 15 μm. The objects are composed of fine mesh. They contain not only gold but also platinum, iron, and other elements mixed together.

rather at the surface or near surface areas. And it was not happening everywhere in the cathode, but only in certain localized regions. What could this mean?

Up to this point we have considered the hydrogen electrode reaction as it pertains to the entire surface of the electrode, without considering what differences might occur from one location on the surface to another. Regarding the previous discussion of hydrogen overpotential, it should be noted that overpotential also varies, and it cannot be measured locally with precision. For example, at one spot on the surface hydrogen recombination overpotential might be at one level, while discharge overpotential is at another, but these components of overpotential have not yet been separately measured.

The debate is about changes in potential in the cathode considered as a whole. The relative percentages of recombination and discharge overpotential for the whole cathode on average have been measured. This average would apply to each spot on the cathode if the cathode surface were uniform, but in reality it may be taken for granted that the metal surface on the microscopic scale is never uniform. As noted previously, it has grain boundaries, defects, protrusions, contaminants and various other dislocations. When the hydrogen recombination occurs around these formations, obviously the reaction is affected by them and is variable from place to place. For example, electrons tend to concentrate around a protrusion, and they make some reactions occur more easily. Because some reactions occur more readily, these reactions, in turn, suppress other reactions. When discharge potential increases, recombination potential must decrease.

When hydrogen is produced at a protrusion, the discharge reaction will be enhanced, the recombination reaction will be suppressed, and the percent of total voltage taken by each changes. Suppose total overpotential is 1.2 volts, with current density at 0.2 amperes per square centimeter. In ordinary, uniform areas on the cathode surface, discharge and recombination overpotentials will be 1.05 volts and 0.15 volts respectively. Near a protrusion discharge occurs more readily, so discharge and recombination overpotentials might be 0.7 and 0.5 volts, which would yield hydrogen pressure reaching 10^{17} atmospheres. This far and away exceeds the 10^{11} atmospheres of pressure in the center of the sun.

When the difference between the percentages of discharge and recombination overpotential changes slightly, pressure changes drastically. If recombination overpotential goes as high as 0.7 volts, it would reach 10^{23} atmospheres, easily surpassing the pressure at the core of a neutron star.

This discussion of overpotential is not mere theory; with titanium, total overpotential was measured at 1.2 volts, which, based on the Tafel equations, should produce pressure as high as 10^{10} atmospheres. (See "Tafel" in glossary.) Under such conditions, protons and electrons may not exist as hydrogen atoms; they would be more stable combined as a neutron. (This reaction would be the inverse of a beta decay. As noted above, electron capture in a proton has been confirmed experimentally with a powerful accelerator at Stanford University.) With sufficiently high energy levels, these neutral particles might be forced into the nuclei of the atoms that form the cathode metal.

When this happens, with light water electrolysis one or two neutrons will enter the nucleus, and with deuterium two to four neutrons will go in. If neutrons do get in, we can compute how the reaction will then proceed, depending upon the stability of the nucleus and the energy of the neutrons. This does not always form elements heavier than palladium. To the contrary, the nucleus will sometimes become unstable, and nuclear fission will occur. We can predict the statistical likelihood of each outcome.

Future Developments

The biggest problems facing researchers up to now have been to produce high pressure when the experiment begins, and to maintain that pressure over an extended period. Once this is accomplished, a reaction will surely follow, and this reaction should not be anything particularly novel. It should be explicable according to present theory as a form of fission.

There is a big difference in the elements and the isotopic distribution of palladium in samples that produce excess heat compared with those which do not. From this fact, that the reaction can go in so many ways, it is clear that in order to produce large excess heat we will need rigorous control over the process. We have to make it easy for the heat reaction to occur. We must adjust many parameters like the surface preparation, the dopants in the metal, and electrolysis conditions. We must build up a data base showing how each change affects the reaction. Learning to control the reaction perfectly will take a lot of time and much hard work.

The biggest stumbling block may be the term "cold fusion" itself, which seems to engender hysterical opposition on its own. It seems to compel people to say that the issue must be long settled—especially people who have done no experiments and made no observations themselves. They write disparaging articles based on mere opinion.

Of course cold fusion was abnormal from the start. It was considered fit subject matter only for an ephemeral "science de jour"—a passing fancy. Year after year, it appears to have produced only murky conclusions. However it is not right to dismiss the results and settle the matter by throwing cold fusion into a box labeled "pathological science."

As discussed above, we now have clear-cut examples of data showing reaction products. By paying close attention and performing detailed, rigorous experiments, scientists have finally improved replicability and shown reaction products. From here, by varying even more parameters, changing experimental conditions, and accumulating even more data, we think that we can reveal every aspect of this reaction.

EPILOGUE

In 1997 the environment surrounding the cold fusion debate changed for the better. Not only in Japan, but elsewhere in the world we see a new spirit of willingness to look at this field. I have been invited to attend four conferences here and overseas, in the U.S., Korea and Russia. It was my first opportunity to visit the latter two countries.

I was invited to Korea in May, where I gave a lecture at Ajow University in Suwon City, about forty kilometers south of Seoul. The audience was particularly interested in my discourse on the generation and control of heat. The main point of my talk was that nobody has yet found a way to control the reaction, and that in order to do this we must learn more about the mechanism by investigating the reaction products and discovering their interrelationships. Five or six hundred people came to the lecture. Seventy or 80 percent of them were students, and they had a deep understanding of the topic. After I finished speaking, they asked many penetrating questions. Some twenty people lined up with question after question, enough to overrun the allotted time.

The student's enquiries made me realize that they already knew a great deal about cold fusion. They knew more about reaction mechanisms and recent developments than any audience I had addressed up to that time in previous conferences. Their pursuit of knowledge is so serious—almost to a fault—it gave me a sense that Korea will continue its rapid development for a long time to come.

No sooner did I return from Korea when I was off to Russia. I was in Moscow from the end of May through the first part of June. From the airplane I looked down over the snowy plains of Siberia, and the sight brought back recollections of my trips to Texas. The Texas desert and the Siberian frozen steppes both appear to stretch endlessly. They both impart feelings of awesome strength and confront human beings with the earthy rawness of nature. This boundless space must have a profound effect on the culture and thinking of the two nations. They have much in common: their tenacity, and the fact that both are populated by many different races coexisting on the same land. The soil seems to support many different ways of thinking. In both countries many scientists still quietly continue research on cold fusion, and are still devising new scientific techniques and making new discoveries.

Certainly, Japan is also doing this research. But the truth is, Japan's methods and theory are largely dependent upon the U.S. and Russia. In their reserves of hidden resources, they totally outclass Japan.

Moscow, the first place I visited, is still clearly engulfed in economic chaos, but I sensed something dynamic in its cultural strength and historical legacy. To be sure, the universities in particular are in a dreadful state financially, yet the depth of the research they are doing, the diversity, and creativity are admirable.

In Moscow I gave a lecture before an audience of sixty people. They were all researchers, and their questions were rather technical. They were particularly interested in theory. The lecture was thirty minutes long and we spent twice as much time as that during the question and answer period afterwards. Once again I was surprised by the depths of their interest. The rapid fire questions were in Russian. We had to speak in English through an interpreter. They grew impatient with this awkward procedure and they ended up writing on the blackboard directly in front of me. I was overwhelmed by their enthusiasm.

Research in Russia was once on the cutting edge, but details were never leaked to the outside world. Now, because of economic difficulties many researchers have fled to other countries, carrying secrets with them, in some cases leaving only a few people to continue the work within Russia.

Of course, even now, you might hear rumors while on a tourist trip or while attending a conference, but it is as impossible as it ever was to really get into the back rooms of the labs, or to learn the inner details of their research. The only thing you can do is learn about part of their research, by sponsoring it, or by engaging in joint projects. Below, I list some of the examples of alleged or reported research that I found extraordinary, although I cannot vouch for them and I cannot put definite names and specific places to most of these accounts.

Regarding cold fusion, Russian researchers claim that more than twenty years before the 1989 Fleischmann and Pons announcement, similar research was reported in Russia. They say it did not cause a sensation because the thesis was written in Russian and because it did not refer to anything like "cold fusion," so it did not attract much attention. It certainly does appear that when you follow up on references, you soon find many dissertations and conference reports. It shows how unlimited—and inscrutable—this country can be. In areas with possible connection to military applications, perhaps even now a great deal of research is going on completely under wraps.

Plasma fusion rocket engines are said to be under development in Russia. This is not a novel idea, but it has not been made practical in any country yet. This research is being performed in cooperation with the U.S., and it has probably reached the stage where prototypes are being operated. The problem is the construction materials are not durable enough. The same is true of conventional plasma fusion.

For a long time I have wanted to experiment with a special kind of material: mono-isotopic pure palladium. This is not only "pure" in the ordinary chemical sense of having low contamination. It is special material made up of just one isotope. Palladium has six stable isotopes. The number of protons is the same in every isotope of an element, but the number of neutrons varies. The percent of each isotope found in nature (natural abundances) varies: palladium-102 is rare; palladium-105 is more common.

Mass Number	Neutrons	Natural Abundance Percentages
102	56	1.2
104	58	8.7
105	59	20.5
106	60	22.3
108	62	15.6
110	64	10.5

An isotopically pure sample would be made up entirely of only one isotope (for example, all palladium-102, or palladium-104). I searched around, but I could not find a supplier of mono-isotopic material in Japan. The only possibility is to purchase samples from America. However, the prices are preposterous; they make gold and platinum look dirt cheap. In Russia, however, it is said that you can obtain such materials quite easily and cheaply. I was shown actual samples which were claimed to be 99.99% pure. That is astounding, if true. Unfortunately I was not able to take a sample for testing.

Back in Japan

Soon after I returned to Japan, a research conference was held at Iwate University in Morioka City, sponsored by Professor Yamada of the Engineering Department, about the very subject I have been working on: transmutation in solid state materials. The meeting was held in a secluded hall in a park near the Kitakami River. There were twelve papers concentrating on transmutation, every one of them with data to corroborate the possibility of transmutation. Even in Japan we are at last making a serious effort to come to grips with the reaction mechanism.

IECEC-32

IECEC-32, the 32nd Intersociety Energy Conversion Engineering Conference was held from July 27 to August 1, 1997 in Honolulu Hawaii, at the Hilton Hawaiian Village Hotel. The presentations were mainly from the U.S.; from Japan only Ohmori of the Catalysis Research Center and I attended. There were 30 participants and 20 papers in the cold fusion section. Nothing especially new was reported. I found it notable that most of the papers were focused on transmutation. All sorts of metals were used as cathodes in electrolysis, and elements appeared on the surface that did not appear to be contamination. Mainly, various forms of radiation were described, and the connection between heat production and products like helium, tritium, and so on was mentioned. *

The Saint

On the airplane going back to Japan the in-flight movie was particularly hilarious to me. It was a 1997 American movie called "The Saint," and the theme was none other than cold fusion. The setting was Russia—Moscow, to be sure—which suffers from a continuous severe energy shortage. The story centers around a cold fusion discovery made by a beautiful lady scientist in England, plus a love story between her and a spy who is trying to find out about her discovery. They go for broke to escape from the Russian mafia bad guys who are out to get the secret and control the world's energy. In the end the cold fusion reactor turns on and works splendidly, and everyone lives happily ever after. It seemed altogether too much of a coincidence that I had recently returned from lecturing on cold fusion in Moscow, and here I was seeing a movie about cold fusion in Moscow. If ever in real life I can make a cold fusion reaction work as well as the one in the movie, my labor will not have been in vain.

---

*IECEC is a mainstream conference sponsored by the American Institute of Chemical Engineers (AICE), the American Nuclear Society (ANS), the Society of Automotive Engineers (SAE), the American Institute of Aeronautics and Astronautics (AIAA), the American Society of Mechanical Engineers (ASME), and the Institute of Electrical and Electronic Engineers (IEEE).

POSTSCRIPT

When I submit a paper to a journal with the term "cold fusion" in it, or I use that term in conversation with other scientists, I instantly sense their unease. I can see they are thinking "something's fishy." From that moment on they refuse to deal with me squarely.

Perhaps this is caused by a recent trend among scientists. Many scientists have become, in large measure, like talk-show critics who try to avoid the dangers inherent in new experiments and new research. I cannot escape the feeling that this is typical of our modern era, in which young people have drifted away from science and scientists themselves have lost their curiosity to explore unknown territory.

People seem to crave a risk-free, emotionless career. As a researcher I want exactly the opposite experience. The feeling of uncertainty and suspense encountered when one is seeking to uncover the truth is the very essence of scientific research and it is a sensation I treasure.

Six months after cold fusion was announced, the American Department of Energy denounced it. In Japan, the people who are considered authorities blindly emulated the attitude of the Americans, as they invariably do, and they too pontificated against cold fusion. Perhaps it was inevitable that most people would assume the claims are cock and bull nonsense. In keeping with the tide of the times, countless books and articles have been published attacking cold fusion.

The very act of researching cold fusion has become scandalous. People who do the research are no longer considered scientists; they are regarded as being "beyond the pale." But this is base prejudice rooted in mistakes made by people who know nothing about the research, and who refuse to learn anything about it. Those who make the effort to carefully examine positive results from major experiments will be forced to conclude that something stupendous is happening in this field.

At the outset, people thought we would soon have a theory which would make it easy to control the reaction and extract as much energy as you like from a test tube. It turned out the reaction mechanism was far from simple. It now appears that a minuscule reaction occurs at the interface between the solvent and the sample material—actually, it occurs in restricted spots within that area—a fact which many researchers have overlooked until now.

Work of this nature requires long-term support. Scientific research seldom yields speedy conclusions. Trial and error exploration, which is sometimes like walking through a pitch dark room, gradually leads to results, which shape theories, which in turn corroborate experiments. From this cycle of routine, modest toil—experiments, theory, more experiments—science finally reveals splendid truths.

This research is in its infancy. The road to conclusive results is arduous and many hardships must be faced along the way. But with the fine efforts of many talented researchers, I firmly believe the day is nigh when the intricacies and complexities of the entire discipline will be clearly exposed to all through an open vista.

BIBLIOGRAPHY

References

1. Fleischmann, Martin and Stanley Pons, "Electrochemically Induced Nuclear Fusion of Deuterium," *J. Electroanal. Chem.*, 261 (1989) 301-308.
2. Mizuno, T., T. Akimoto, and N. Sato. "Neutron Evolution from Annealed Palladium Cathode in LiOD-D_2O Solution," *Denki kagaku*, 57, No. 7, (1989) 742-743.
3. Mizuno, T., T. Akimoto, K. Azumi, and N. Sato, "Tritium Evolution during Cathodic Polarization of Palladium Electrode in D_2O Solution," *Denki kagaku*, 59, No. 9, 1991.
4. Yamaguchi, E. and T. Nishioka, "Direct Evidence for Nuclear Fusion Reactions in Deuterated Palladium, Frontiers of Cold Fusion," *Frontiers or Science Series No. 4*, Universal Academy Press, (1993) 179-188. Unfortunately, Yamaguchi was not able to replicate these results during extensive testing over several years at IMRA. See: E. Yamaguchi and H. Sugiura, IMRA Europe, France, "Progress Report on the Study of Excess Heat and Nuclear Products by the 'In-vacuo' Method run at IMRA Europe," *Proc. Seventh International Conf. Cold Fusion*, Vancouver, BC, Canada, April 19-24, 1998
5. Mizuno, T. and M. Enyo. "Sorption of Hydrogen On and In Hydrogen-Absorbing Metal in Electrochemical Environments," *Modern Aspects of Electrochemistry*, Vol. 30, (1996).
6. Iwahara, H. T., Esaka, H. Uchida and N. Meda, *Solid State Ionics*, 3/4, (1981) 359; H. Iwahara, H. Uchida, K, Kondo and K. Ogaki, *J. Electrochem.* Soc., 135, (1988) 529; T. Yajima, K. Koide, K. Yamamoto and H. Iwahara, *Denki Kagaku*, 58, (1990) 547.
7. Oriani, R. A. "An Investigation of Anomalous Thermal Power Generation from a Proton-conducting Oxide," *Fusion Technology*, 30 (1996) 281-287.
8. Mizuno, T., K. Inoda, T. Akimoto, K. Azumi, M. Kitaichi, K. Kurokawa. T. Ohmori and M. Enyo. "Anomalous Gamma Peak Evolution from SrCe Solid State Electrolyte Charged in D_2 Gas," *Int. J. Hydrogen Energy*, Vol. 22, No.1 (1997) 23.
9. G. H. Miley and J. A. Patterson, "Nuclear Transmutations in Thin Film Nickel Coating Undergoing Electrolysis," *Infinite Energy*, Vol. 2, No. 9 (1996).

10. T. Mizuno, T. Ohmori, K. Kurokawa, T. Akimoto, M. Kitaichi, M. Enyo, "Anomalous isotopes found in cathode precipitate after electrolysis," *Denkikagaku oyobi kougaku buturi kagaku,* Vol. 65, No. 11 (1996) 1160 - 1165.

11. Conte E., (1) 1992, "Quantum Ergodic Systems and Biquaternion Quantum Mechanics," *Physics Essays,* 5 pp. 70-74, (2) 1993, "An Example of wavefunction Reduction by Biquaternions," *Physics Essays,* 6, pp. 532-535; (3) 1993, "On a Generalization of Quantum Mechanics by Biquaternions, h. J.4, pp. 261; (4) 1994, "Wave function reduction in Biquaternion Quantum Mechanics," *Physics Essays,* 7, pp. 429-435; (5) 995, "On a Generalization of Schrodinger Equation in BQM," *Physics Essays,* 8, pp. 52-59; (6) 1995, "New Paula Matrices in BQM," *Physics Essays,* 8, 605-614; (7) 1996, "An A. Fine Criticism to Quantum Problems," *Physics Essays,* 9, pp. 141-147.; (8) "On a Generalization of the Physical Laws by Biquaternions;" "An Application to the Generalization of Minkowski Space Time," *Physics Essays,* 20; Conte E., 1996, "Meccanica Quantistica Biquaternionica" Vol. 1, edited by Pitagora Editrice, Bologna, Italy. This volume also contains a diskette in English regarding cold fusion and BQM.

12. Maoka, T. and M. Enyo, *Electrochmica Acta,* 26, No.5, 615 (1981); M. Enyo and T. Maoka, *J. Electroanal. Chem.,* 108, 277 (1980).

There are many books and papers on the subject of cold fusion. Here are books that appeared soon after cold fusion was announced:

Peat, F. D. *Cold Fusion,* Contemporary Books, 1989.

Mallove, E. F. *Fire from Ice: Searching for the Truth Behind the Cold Fusion Furor,* John Wiley & Sons, Inc., 1991. (Now available from Infinite Energy Press, P.O. Box 2816, Concord, NH 03302-2816).

Yamaguchi, E. (In Japanese) *Sikenkan no naka no taiyou* ("Capturing the Sun in a Test Tube"), Kodansha, 1993.

Books that express a negative view. Here is a typical example:

Taubes, G. *Bad Science,* Random House, 1993.

COLD FUSION CHRONOLOGY*

1967

Throughout the late '60s and early '70s Martin Fleischmann and his colleagues conduct research on the separation of hydrogen and deuterium isotopes, work that leads in the 1980s to cold fusion experiments.

Mizuno is at Hokkaido University, Nuclear Energy Research Department.

January - Mizuno restores neutron beam generator to working order and utilizes it in his attempts to load hydrogen into titanium (part of his thesis work).

1968

March 13 - Mizuno produces his graduate thesis "Absorption by Metals of Deuterons Implanted by an Ion Accelerator."

1978

Russian physicist B.A. Mamyrin observes anomalies in the concentrations of helium-3 and helium-4 in metals, work that later influences Steve Jones and his colleagues at Brigham Young University (BYU).

B. Stanley Pons examines isotopic separation in palladium electrodes and is puzzled by some of his results.

The mid to late 1970s herald the beginnings of inertial confinement (laser) fusion efforts.

August - Mizuno, working with Kurachi, observes evaporation of electrolyte in a Pd - D_2O - D_2SO_4 electrolytic cell after input power is cut off. 200 cc of liquid disappears. This they eventually disregard as being an "unsolvable mystery."

1980

U.S. Magnetic Fusion Energy Engineering Act of 1980 recommends a doubling of the magnetic fusion budget within seven years.

1981

May - Mizuno, working with Mori from the Nuclear High Vacuum Research Department at Hokkaido discovers x-rays when loading titanium with deuterium. They

*Prepared by staff of Infinite Energy Magazine.

confirm that the radiation is originating from the electrolytic cell.

1983

Alcator-C tokamak at MIT is the first tokamak to exceed the minimum Lawson parameter for breakeven (if fuel were deuterium-tritium).

July - Norio Sato suggests that Mizuno apply to work with John Bockris.

1984

Pons and Fleischmann begin their collaboration on an electrochemical experiment to search for evidence for cold fusion.

March - Mizuno begins work at Texas A&M on analysis of electrochemical reactions on metal surfaces.

1985

Geneva Summit between Reagan and Gorbachev launches the ITER program to build an "International Thermonuclear Experimental Reactor" involving the US, USSR, Japan and the European community.

1986

April-May - Stephen Jones (BYU) and his colleagues begin planning cold fusion experiments with metals.

Jones and Clint van Siclen publish paper on "piezonuclear fusion."

1987

Johann Rafelski and Steven Jones publish an article in the July 1987 issue of *Scientific American* titled, "Cold Nuclear Fusion." They describe the process of muon-catalyzed fusion reactions.

1988

TFTR tokamak at Princeton attains a plasma temperature of 300 million degrees K. Both JET tokamak in England and TFTR approach breakeven conditions.

1989

February 23 - Pons and Fleischmann visit Jones' group at Brigham Young University. Jones mentions intent to publish an article on his research and to deliver his paper to the American Physical Society Meeting on May 4, 1989. Pons and Fleischmann want to spend more time - perhaps 18 months longer - on their experiments before going public.

March 11 - Pons and Fleischmann submit their paper on cold fusion to the *Journal of Electroanalytical Chemistry and Interfacial Electrochemistry*.

March 23 - Fleischmann and Pons announce at a press conference at the University of Utah in Salt Lake City that a "simple experiment results in sustained fusion at room temperature for the first time." The story is first reported by the *Financial Times* in England and the *Wall Street Journal* in the US, triggering a media avalanche of coverage that lasts for months. Scientists around the world immediately begin efforts to confirm or reject the Utah claims.

Stephen E Jones submits his paper to Nature.

March 24 - Mizuno sees newspaper article about Fleischmann & Pons announcement and decides to start his own experiment.

Governor Norm Bangerter of Utah announces the convening of a special session of the state legislature to approve $5 million to start an institute for cold fusion research.

March 31 - Mizuno, working with Akimoto, launches a search for reaction products in his electrolytic cell. This search proves fruitless.

March-April - Major cold fusion experimental efforts begin in Japan and India.

April 7 - Utah legislature passes cold fusion research legislation.

April 8 - The University of Utah legislature meets to consider $5 million appropriation for cold fusion research and development. Money is set aside, not to be used unless the University of Utah experiments are confirmed.

April 10 - Researchers at Texas A&M University claim to have duplicated the Pons and Fleischmann experiment (this one group's claim is later found to be a mistake).

Researchers at Georgia Tech announce the detection of neutrons from an electrochemical cell. (A claim subsequently retracted three days later.)

Pons and Fleischmann paper on cold fusion appears in the *Journal of Electroanalytical Chemistry and Interfacial Electrochemistry*.

April 12 - Meeting of the American Chemical Society in Dallas, Texas, is attended by some 7,000 chemists; Pons defends the alleged fusion breakthrough.

Prof. Peter L. Hagelstein at MIT announces his explanation of cold fusion as "coherent fusion." MIT announces that it has applied for patents related to Hagelstein's theories.

Professor Keith Johnson of MIT's Department of Materials Science and Engineering announces his theory to explain the University of Utah results on the basis of "dynamical John-Teller" chemical bonding, while acknowledging that small amounts of nuclear fusion could be taking place in the palladium electrode. He is first to suggest publicly that heat may come from light water tests too.

April 14 - University of Utah chemistry professors Cheves T. Walling and John T. Simons announce their theory to explain the Pons-Fleischmann experiments.

Georgia Tech researchers retract their claimed neutron detection.

April 17 - At a University of Utah press conference, Pons announces that results of mass spectroscopy reveals quantities of helium-4 are being produced by their electrochemical cells.

April 18 - Italian physicist Francesco Scaramuzzi, with a group at the Italian Atomic Energy Authority at Frascati claims success in detecting neutrons from cold fusion using a titanium metal infused under pressure with deuterium.

Robert Huggins at Stanford University says he has obtained excess heat in an electrochemical cell with heavy water, but not in one with light water.

April 21 - "Prof A" and "Prof B" hold press conference denouncing CF and using Mizuno's negative results (see March 31 above) to substantiate this.

April 24 - Secretary of Energy Admiral James Watkins establishes a review panel to evaluate cold fusion claims. Directs DoE's National Laboratories to conduct cold fusion research investigations.

April 26 - Members of the U.S. House of Representatives Committee on Science, Space and Technology hear request from the University of Utah for quick approval of $25 million to help commercialize their alleged fusion process.

April 27 - A paper by Steven E. Jones and seven colleagues appears in *Nature,* titled "Observations of Cold Nuclear Fusion in Condensed Matter." Editorial by John Maddox in *Nature* is skeptical of Pons-Fleischmann cold fusion claims.

April 28 - Yale University-Brookhaven National Laboratory collaboration reports detecting no nuclear products from electrochemical cells after three weeks of trying.

Researchers at Case Western Reserve University report excess heat and tritium generation in electrochemical cells.

May 1-2 - Researchers at MIT Plasma Fusion Center say they have found serious flaws in the neutron emissions data reported by Pons and Fleischmann; say that Pons and Fleischmann were unlikely to have detected neutrons. At a meeting of the American Physical Society in Baltimore, Maryland, physicists and chemists roundly criticize and mock the work of Pons and Fleischmann.

May 8 - At meeting of the Electrochemical Society in Los Angeles, Pons and Fleischmann defend their experiments against criticism, but back off of their claims to have detected neutrons.

May 18 - An extended scientific correspondence by researchers at MIT's Plasma Fusion Center appears in *Nature,* critiquing the original Pons and Fleischmann neutron data and finding it to be flawed.

May 23-25 - The first conference dedicated exclusively to cold fusion is held in Santa Fe, New Mexico and draws some 500 participants.

June 15 - Harwell Laboratory in England stops work in cold fusion experiments.

June 26 - Los Alamos National Laboratory scientists announce finding tritium in cold fusion experiments.

MIT Plasma Fusion Center holds "Wake for Cold Fusion" party, despite not having analyzed its cold fusion calorimetry data.

Late June - Release of funding by Utah State Fusion Energy Advisory Council to establish National Cold Fusion Institute.

July 12 - Interim report by ERAB panel of DOE finds no good evidence for cold fusion and rejects a formal research center for cold fusion.

July 22 - Mizuno attends International Electrochemical Society Meeting where cold fusion is relegated to a separate session. Despite papers presented by Fleischmann & Pons and Bockris, he regards it as mainly a "media event."

July 31 - First formal conference in Japan, held under the auspices of the International Electrochemical Society, where cold fusion results are presented.

October 12 - Mizuno is invited to speak to a conference of the Japan Physics Society at Miyasaki University. He presents his paper and is heckled by certain parties within the audience.

October - Mizuno begins work on designing a closed cell.

October 19-20 - EPRI/NSF meeting on cold fusion in Washington DC

Electrochemical Society meeting in Hollywood, Florida - cold fusion session

November 8 - Final DoE ERAB report approved, concluding that evidence for cold fusion is not persuasive.

Mizuno continues his research in earnest.

1990

Throughout this and the following year, papers detailing cold fusion replications are published by Fritz Will, Melvin Miles and others.

March - Mizuno resolves the leakage problem in his new closed cell and makes appropriate modifications.

March 28-31 - First Annual Conference on Cold Fusion held in Salt Lake City is attended by over 200 researchers.

Nature magazine (**March 29**) publishes scathing editorial attacks on cold fusion research and prints an article by University of Utah physicist Michael Salamon *et al.* claiming that in 1989 tests they detected no nuclear products coming from Pons' cells.

Mizuno attends First International Conference on Cold Fusion (ICCF1), Salt Lake City, Utah where many researchers report positive CF replication results.

June - Mizuno moves his closed cell to the underground laboratory at Hokkaido for testing.

June 15 - Publication in *Science* of a lengthy expose by journalist Gary Taubes in which he strongly suggests that high levels of tritium found in Texas A&M University cold fusion experiments were the result of fraudulent spiking of the cells.

July 23 - Bruce Liebert and Bor Yann Liaw and colleagues at the University of Hawaii report multi-watt excess power output from electrochemical cells incorporating molten salts and deuterium. Results reported at the cold fusion sessions of the World Hydrogen Energy Conference.

July 25 - A comprehensive paper on excess-heat measurements in electrochemical cells is published by Fleischmann, Pons, et al in the *Journal of Electroanalytical Chemistry*.

October 22-24 - Conference on "Anomalous Nuclear Effects in Deuterium /Sold Systems" at Brigham Young University. Major confirming evidence presented that finds energetic tritons in cold fusion experiments. Conference produces clinching proof that cold fusion can occur in deuterated systems without being catalyzed by muons.

November 7- Review meeting in Salt Lake City of the Fusion Energy Advisory Council. Stanley Pons attends after returning from an alleged "disappearance" in Europe.

Mid-December - Review panel gives NCFI operations generally favorable critique.

1991

February - Researcher, Azumi, joins Mizuno. They discover tritium following analysis of electrolyte.

March 17 - Sunday *New York Times* front page: Frank Close book *Too Hot to Handle*, profiled - accusations of ethical violations against Pons and Fleischmann. Mallove's book *Fire From Ice* was never reviewed by the *New York Times*.

March 22-26 - First Soviet National Conference on Cold Fusion, Dubna-Moscow. Research at 45 institutes reported, 80 papers submitted.

March 24 - Faults observed in the recombiner of Mizuno's closed cell, small frequent explosions occur.

April 6 - Mizuno observes an astonishing heat-after-death incident (see separate timeline on this event in the preface)

April - Mizuno meets with Araki, adviser to Nissho Iwai Corporation.

April 24 - Mayer-Reitz "hydron" theory of cold fusion announced.

Randell Mills announces "shrinking hydrogen atom" (hydrino) theory and experimental evidence for significant excess heat in light water, nickel, potassium carbonate cells.

Late May - Publication of Eugene Mallove's book, *Fire from Ice: Searching for the Truth Behind the Cold Fusion Furor,* (John Wiley & Sons).

June - Mizuno finds black deposition on cathode and scrapes it away, believing it to be contamination, an action he later regrets.

Eugene Mallove resigns MIT News Office post citing ethical violations by MIT researchers who attacked cold fusion.

June 29-July 4 - Second Annual Conference on Cold Fusion (ICCF2), Como, Italy. Mizuno does not attend. He is busy with his experiments.

June 30 - National Cold Fusion Institute closes.

August 18 - Eugene Mallove files formal request for investigation of mishandling of data in 1989 MIT PFC cold fusion calorimetry experiment.

September - Publication of article on Mizuno's work in *Bungei Shunju* by F. Nakano entitled "The Reality of Cold Fusion can no longer be denied."

December 18 - Martin Fleischmann speaks at MIT on cold fusion research.

1992

January 2 - Researcher, Andrew Riley, killed in explosion at SRI during cold fusion experiment.

January 27 - ISEM, IEEE meeting of cold fusion researchers, Nagoya, Japan. Akito Takahashi of Osaka University reports massive excess heat and low-level neutrons.

March - Publication by Drs. Noninski of positive results in excess heat measurement in nickel, light water, potassium carbonate system.

April 1 - Eugene Mallove testifies favoring cold fusion research before Subcommittee on Energy and Water of the US House Appropriations Committee.

Final letter from MIT President Vest closing MIT PFC calorimetry matter without final resolution.

April 15 - Professor Akita Takahashi gives seminar at MIT on his heat and neutron producing cold fusion experiments.

May - Mizuno discovers solid state ceramic proton conductors and ponders their use in his experiments.

MIT PFC published single-author "Technical Appendix" to sixteen-author 1989 cold fusion calorimetry experiment report, expands error limits.

July 10 - Japan's MITI announces major funding of cold fusion research.

Mid-July - Publication of John Huizenga's book *Cold Fusion: Scientific Fiasco of the Century* (University of Rochester Press).

July 27 - Edmund Storms of Los Alamos National Laboratory announces replication

of Takahashi excess heat.

August - Dr. Mitchell R. Swartz publishes "Reexamination of a Key Cold Fusion Experiment: 'Phase-II' Calorimetry by the MIT Plasma Fusion Center" in *Fusion Facts*. Analysis finds numerous faults in the analysis, as well as proof that data were inappropriately handled.

September 24 - McKubre of SRI speaks about excess heat results at MIT.

Late September - Electrochemical Society Meeting in Japan; many excess heat reports.

October 21-25 - Third International Conference on Cold Fusion (ICCF3), Nagoya, Japan. Numerous results confirm reproducibility of excess heat and nuclear phenomena.

Mizuno presents paper on the effect of deuterium loading on excess heat.

November 17 - NTT Laboratories announces $565,000 "Cold Fusion Kit."

December 3-10 - Dr. Reiko Notoya of Hokkaido University at MIT to demonstrate her light water cold fusion experiment.

1993

Throughout this year, Mizuno concentrates on work with proton conductors.

March - Mizuno's paper on Anomalous Isotopic Distribution submitted to journals in Japan and overseas.

March 25 - Congressman Dick Swett (NH) and Eugene Mallove testify before the House Appropriations Committee Subcommittee on Energy and Water to ask for funding for a National Academy of Sciences review of cold fusion.

May 5 - Fusion Energy Hearings before House Subcommittee on Energy of House Science, Space and Technology Committee—cold fusion researchers receive a warm reception.

June - Publication of Gary Taubes' book *Bad Science: The Short Life and Weird Times of Cold Fusion*, (Random House)

Mizuno experiments with different metal cathodes.

June 24 - World premier of Canadian Broadcasting Corporation's "The Secret Life of Cold Fusion."

August - *Popular Science* publishes high-profile, objective account of latest cold fusion developments—a cover story by *Wall Street Journal* Reporter Jerry Bishop.

September - Hydrosonic Pump water cavication technology emerges as a significant probable excess-energy producing device. The horizons of the cold fusion field expand dramatically.

November-December - Mizuno visits SRI International

December 6-9 - Fourth International Conference on Cold Fusion (ICCF4), Maui, Hawaii, sponsored by the Electric Power Research Institute.

Mizuno is unimpressed at the lack of new reports. He regards this conference as uninspiring apart from details of the research of others using proton conductors and reports of transmutation from Russian workers.

"Cold Fusion" magazine is launched, initiated by Eugene Mallove, Jed Rothwell, Chris Tinsley, Larry Forsley and others in the cold fusion field. Three issues are published. (All editors leave WGI publishing firm in June 1994 because of chaos in WGI management. Former editors begin preparations for a new publication, *Infinite Energy*.)

1994

January 1 - Mizuno concentrates on reducing cell contamination.

February - Piantelli-Focardi-Habel announce new ordinary hydrogen-nickel high temperature excess heat results.

March 21 - Landmark CBC(Canadian Broadcasting Corp.) and BBC (British Broadcaasting Corp.) programs on cold fusion - "Too Close to the Sun."

April - Mizuno designs his new cell. Vastly superior data collection system introduced.

May 24-26 - International Symposium on Cold Fusion and Advanced Energy Sources, Minsk, Belarus.

May/June- MIT *Technology Review* cover story, "Warming Up to Cold Fusion, " by Dr. Edmund Storms; severely critical letters from MIT faculty in subsequent issue.

June - Professor Keith Johnson of the MIT Department of Materials Science announces that his techno- thriller movie script, "Breaking Symmetry," will become a feature produced by a major Hollywood studio.

October - E-Quest Sciences announces large amounts of helium production in test of ultrasonic cold fusion reactor at Los Alamos National Laboratory.

Y. Arata and Y.C. Zhang in Japan publish a new "double cathode" method of reliably producing the Pons-Fleischmann excess heat effect.

1995

January - Mizuno sends sample proton conductors to Oriani.

January 21 - "Cold Fusion Day" at MIT - an Independent Activities Period (IAP) Program.

February 14 - Mizuno receives palladium analysis results from independent laboratories, revealing the existence of "new" elements. (See text for details of laboratories and elements found)

April 9-13 - Fifth International Conference on Cold Fusion (ICCF5), Monte Carlo, Monaco.

June 17 - First ILENR Conference (International Low Energy Nuclear Reactions) held at Texas A&M.

June 19 - Mizuno presents paper at above on his use of proton conductors and resultant transmutation.

September - European Patent Office gives notice that it will grant the Pons-Fleischmann Patent "Method and Apparatus for Power Generation."

October 1-5 - 16th Biannual Symposium on Fusion Energy, SOFE '95 (Champaign, Illinois); CETI (Clean Energy Technologies, Inc.) demonstrates Patterson Power Cell at 80:1 power ratio.

November - Mizuno discovers the "eruptions" on Ohmori's gold cathodes.

December 5-7 - CETI demonstrates Patterson Power Cell at Power Gen '95 in Anaheim, California: 1,300 watts out, 1.4 watts in.

1996

January - Mizuno examines cathodes and finds unusual elements present.

January 20 - Cold Fusion & New Energy Symposium sponsored by *Infinite Energy* magazine at Cambridge Marriott Hotel.

February 7 - ABC TV programs "Good Morning America" and "Nightline" feature cold fusion and the Patterson Power Cell.

March 26 - Oriani, at the University of Minnesota, obtains excess heat using Mizuno's proton conductors.

April - Mizuno's paper on isotopic anomalies accepted by *Denkikagaku oyobi kougaku buturi kagaku*

September 13 - Second ILENR Conference, Texas - problems with venue at Texas A&M, refused permission to hold conference on campus as cold fusion is "impossible". Conference moved to nearby hotel.

Mizuno presents paper on transmutation and is disappointed by the lack of stimulating questions and the apparently blind acceptance of his results.

Bockris announces he will retire the following year. Mizuno is saddened by this and worries what will happen to CF research now that most of the other major workers have also retired.

September - E. Conte sends Mizuno his theory on the cold fusion reaction.

October 13-18 - Sixth International Conference on Cold Fusion (ICCF-6), Hokkaido, Japan.

1997

December - Mizuno's book published in Japanese by Kogakushu.

Mizuno feels there is a new willingness to examine cold fusion. He visits the US, Korea and Russia this year.

July - IECEC-32, Hawaii. The results presented mostly concern transmutation.

1998

April - Collapse of the Japan New Hydrogen Energy Program due to failed management.

Seventh International Conference on Cold Fusion (ICCF7), Vancouver, British Columbia

May 4 - Professor Makoto Okamoto, a leading cold fusion researcher, dies at age 60.

October 11 - Cold Fusion and New Energy Symposium, Manchester, NH

1999

Eighth International Conference on Cold Fusion. Scheculed at a nuclear facility in Italy.

Formation of ^{197}Pt Radioisotopes in Solid State Electrolyte Treated by High Temperature Electrolysis in D$_2$ Gas

(From *Infinite Energy*, Vol. 1, No. 4, September/October 1995)

Tadahiko Mizuno(1), Koich Inoda(2), Tadashi Akimoto(1), Kazuhisa Azumi(1), Masatoshi Kitaichi(1), Kazuya Kurokawa(1), Tadayoshi Ohmori(1) and Michio Enyo(2)

(1)Hokkaido University, Kitaku, North 13 West 8, Sapporo 060 Japan
(2)Hakodata National College of Technology, Tokuracho 14-1, Hakodate 042 Japan

A proton conductor, a solid state electrolyte made from oxide of strontium, cerium, niobium and yttrium, was charged in a hot D$_2$ atmosphere. Anomalous radioisotopes were detected in all samples charged with an alternating current with voltages ranging from 5V to 45V, at temperatures ranging from 400 to 700°C. No radioisotopes were observed in samples charged in a hot H$_2$ atmosphere.

Cold fusion, a nuclear reaction in the solid state, has been confirmed by many experiments. What is most needed now is to obtain the precise, quantitative relationship between each potential nuclear reaction and its corresponding reaction product. We submit that the ideal way to do this is to observe as many parameters as possible simultaneously on-line: heat evolution; neutron emission; tritium generation, and so on. Unfortunately, this is very difficult to do because the phenomenon is so hard to reproduce and control. Even when it has been possible to measure several parameters at once, the amounts of reaction products are very low and often close to or under the limits of detection, making quantitative calibration difficult. Therefore, the best technique has been to analyze radioactive products from samples before and after the experiment, rather than on-line in real time.

In the present work, samples were made from a mixture of metal oxides of Sr, Ce, Y and Nb, according to procedures worked out by Iwahara *et al.*[1,2,3] These powdered oxides were first mixed, and then sintered in an electric furnace at 1400°C in air for 16 hours. The samples were pulverized and mixed, then alcohol was added. They were placed in a

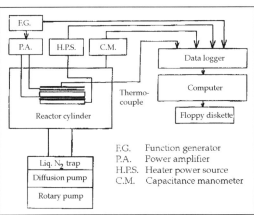

Figure 1. Experimental arrangement. The sample was heated to a constant temperature with an electric heater covered with stainless steel. Electric power was supplied from a stabilized power source. The electric fields (proton driving voltage: EPD) was supplied from a function generator via a power amplifier. Pressure was measured to a capacitance manometer with 0.1 Torr accuracy. Temperature was recorded with 0.1°C accuracy by three thermocouples that were coated with this stainless steel cover. All parameters: EPD (voltage and current), heater power, sample temperature, gas pressure and cylinder wall temperature were recorded in a data logger computer floppy diskette. The reaction cell is a stainless steel cylinder 40 cm long, 20 cm in diameter, with walls 5 mm thick.

press and formed into disks of 20mm diameter and 1mm thickness. These plates were again sintered at 1300-1480°C in air for 16 hours. Sample densities ranged from 3.0 to 5.2. The theoretical density for a perfectly sintered sample is 5.8. Both sides of the sintered sample were coated with porous Pt film by one of two methods: 1) By painting a Pt organic compound and deposition at 700°C; or 2) By coating with Ar sputtered onto Pt in a vacuum. The resulting Pt film thickness was 0.15-0.3 μm. The film is porous and has a very rough surface, and hydrogen gas easily passes through the film to reach the ceramic surface. A schematic of the measurement system is shown in Figure 1 and a schematic of the reactor is shown in Figure 2.

Experimental procedures were as follows: 1) The reactor cylinder is evacuated with rotary pump, followed by a diffusion pump (with liquid N_2 trap) to 2 x 10^{-5} Torr. 2) The temperature of the sample is raised to 400~700°C. 3) Gas is introduced into the cylinder at 0.1~50 Torr. 4)

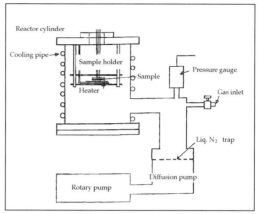

Figure 2. Reactor cylinder. The upper assembly consists of the proton conductor sample, held on both sides with 0.3 mm thick Pt plates, which are in turn sandwiched between 0.3 mm thick Ni plates. Three thermocouples covered with this stainless steel are pushed directly onto the upper part of the upper Pt plate. The Pt plates make electrical contact with the ceramic sample and thermal contact with the thermocouples. This entire assembly is fixed to the lower assembly which is a heater. It consists of spiral resistance heating wire covered with ceramic insulation. EPD power was supplied through copper wires 1.6 mm in diameter. The sample holder is surrounded by Ni plate reflectors. The holder is fixed with four supports made of 6 mm diameter stainless steel, covered by alumina insulators. Four nuts attach under the support rods, pressing the Pt plate, alumina spacer and proton conductor sample tightly against the thermocouple. The components are welded to the cell cover flange that has several electric connectors. The connectors introduce thermocouple, electric power lines for the heater, and electric field supply for the sample.

The sample is charged with EPD power at 5V~ 45V a.c., with frequency set between 10^{-4} and 1 Hz depending on the sample temperature and thickness. 5) All the samples were tested with a Ge(Li) detector for the gamma radiation before and after the electrolysis.

Figure 3. Gamma ray spectrum before the electrolysis (B) and data are accumulated from 0 to 24 hours (A1), for 0 to 48 hours (A2) after electrolysis. (A2-A1) is subtraction from A2 by A1. Gamma ray spectrums were obtained by a four-inch Ge (Li) detector in 4π shield container of 20 cm and 5 mm thickness of Pb outer and Cu inner shields. A multi-channel analyzer of 8000 channels was coincided to 0 to 4000 keV of energy range. A gaussian window was fit to the calculation for the spectrum analysis.

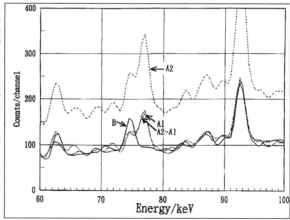

All samples were tested for emissions across the full gamma radiation spectrum. Typical results are shown in Figure 3: B is before electrolysis, A1 and A2 are after electrolysis. A clear peak appeared in Figure 3 (b) at 76.8keV. The peak is only obtained after electrolysis in deuterium gas. It was not observed with hydrogen gas. This peak may be interpreted as coinciding with the radioisotopes ^{197}Pt, ^{153}Sm and ^{155}Sm. However, we do not believe it was caused by ^{153}Sm or ^{155}Sm, because it would have to be accompanied by stronger peaks at 103.2 keV for ^{153}Sm and 104.3 keV for ^{155}Sm. There are no peaks in the 103 keV range. Another peak that may be caused from a second energy spectrum of 191.44 keV was observed. This peak is sometimes difficult to confirm because the intensity is one order of magnitude lower than the first peak. The half-life of the radioisotope synthesized in this experiment is estimated to be ~20 hours. We conclude that the first peak is caused from the 77.35 keV gamma emission of ^{197}Pt radioisotope.

We have confirmed this in five tests with different samples. The effect is 100% reproducible for that same sample. We performed the electrolysis with the same sample in deuterium gas followed by hydrogen gas: the ^{197}Pt peak was only observed with deuterium gas. No trace of ^{197}Pt was detected around the sample holder materials. And there is no ^{197}Pt in the Pt plates used to make electric and thermal contact with the sample, even in samples of the metal as large as 100g. The peak intensity appears to depend upon the deuterium gas pressure. We have not yet determined what, if any, effects temperature, electrolysis voltage, current and sample material may have on the intensity of the ^{197}Pt emission.

^{197}Pt nuclei do not exist in nature. They can only be produced artificially by neutron irradiation, as follows:

$$^{197}_{78}Pt + ^{1}_{0}n \quad ^{197}_{78}Pt \rightarrow ^{197}_{79}Au + \beta- \tag{1}$$

^{197}Pt changes into ^{197}Au by beta decay. Other increases were observed in the spectrum, caused by ^{214}Pb and ^{214}Bi. However, we cannot conclude that other nuclear reactions occurred, because these peaks were already detected before the electrolysis. They may have been caused from contamination absorbed when the sample was heated.

There are no reports of chemical reactions affecting nuclear reactions, and no theory that would allow this. However, evidence of cold fusion gives us a hint as to how these reactions might occur. There are now many reports of cold fusion experiments in which neutron emission, helium isotope evolution, tritium generation, high energetic particle emission, and gamma radiation during hydrogen or deuterium absorption by Pd, Ti, Ni, and some metal oxides were observed.

The total amount of ^{197}Pt nuclear (n) is calculated from the count number and detector efficiency η as follows:

$$n = 2c/\eta \tag{2}$$

η is roughly estimated as being between 10^3 and 10^4. If we assume that all the ^{197}Pt was generated by neutron absorption from one reaction, we can readily estimate the total neutrons from the amount of Pt in the sample and the neutron absorption cross section $\sigma(E)$. The $\sigma(E)$ depends on the neutron energy; it is roughly estimated as 1 barn ($10^{-24}cm^2$) average from thermal to keV range. Total neutrons are then estimated as being between 10^{11} and 10^{12}. However, total neutron emission during the electrolysis is close to or under the background count. It is on the order of 10^2~10^3. These values are 10^8 lower than the results require.

Several metals, including Pt, Pd, Ti and Ni and some alloys (LaNi and TiFe) have a strong catalytic effect on hydrogen. They decompose the H_2 molecule to the H atom and ^+H proton. If we assume that the strong catalytic action also somehow causes a nuclear effect between platinum and deuterium, several reactions can be considered:

$$^{196}_{78}\text{Pt} + D + D \rightarrow \ ^{197}_{78}\text{Pt} + \ ^{3}_{2}\text{He} + 5.46 \text{ MeV} \tag{3}$$

$$^{196}_{78}\text{Pt} + D + D \rightarrow \ ^{196}_{78}\text{Pt} + \ ^{4}_{2}\text{He} + 14.29 \text{ MeV} \tag{4}$$

$$^{196}_{78}\text{Pt} + D + D \rightarrow \ ^{197}_{79}\text{Au} + \ ^{3}_{1}\text{T} + 5.85 \text{ MeV} \tag{5}$$

$$^{196}_{78}\text{Pt} + D + D \rightarrow \ ^{199}_{80}\text{Hg} + \ ^{1}_{0}\text{n} + 8.74 \text{ MeV} \tag{6}$$

$$^{196}_{78}\text{Pt} + D + D \rightarrow \ ^{200}_{80}\text{Hg} + 13.9 \text{ MeV} \tag{7}$$

$$^{196}_{78}\text{Pt} + D + D \rightarrow \ ^{199}_{79}\text{Au} + \ ^{1}_{1}\text{P} \quad ^{199}_{80}\text{Hg} + \beta^{-} + \ ^{1}_{1}\text{P} \tag{8}$$

$$^{196}_{78}\text{Pt} + D \rightarrow \ ^{197}_{78}\text{Pt} + \ ^{1}_{1}\text{P} + 2.20 \text{ MeV} \tag{9}$$

$$^{196}_{78}\text{Pt} + D \rightarrow \ ^{198}_{79}\text{Au} + \ ^{1}_{0}\text{n} + 1.82 \text{ MeV} \tag{10}$$

$$^{196}_{78}\text{Pt} + D \rightarrow \ ^{198}_{79}\text{Au} + 6.07 \text{ MeV} \rightarrow \ ^{198}_{80}\text{Hg} + \beta^{-} \tag{11}$$

^{197}Pt nuclei can be formed by reactions (3) and (9). However, we have sometimes observed very weak neutron emission during electrolysis, which opens up the possibilities for other reactions such as (6) and (10).

The same type of reaction may occur in Pd. There are many reports of reactions with Pd in dry and wet systems. The following formulas have been proposed to explain this:

$$^{n}_{46}\text{Pd} + D + D \rightarrow \ ^{n+1}_{46}\text{Pd} + \ ^{3}_{2}\text{He} + Q \tag{12}$$

$$^{n}_{46}\text{Pd} + D + D \rightarrow \ ^{n+1}_{47}\text{Ag} + \ ^{3}_{1}\text{T} + Q \tag{13}$$

$$^{n}_{46}\text{Pd} + D + D \rightarrow \ ^{n+1}_{47}\text{Ag} + \ ^{3}_{2}\text{He} + Q \tag{14}$$

$$^{n+4}_{47}\text{Cd} + Q \tag{15}$$

$$^{n}_{46}\text{Pd} + D \rightarrow \ ^{n+1}_{46}\text{Pd} + \ ^{1}_{1}\text{P} + Q \tag{16}$$

$$^{n}_{46}\text{Pd} + D \rightarrow \ ^{n+1}_{47}\text{Ag} + \ ^{1}_{0}\text{n} + Q \tag{17}$$

$$^{n}_{46}\text{Pd} + D \rightarrow \ ^{n+2}_{47}\text{Ag} + Q \tag{18}$$

However, Q values are changed with the isotopes of Pd; the value is on the order of few MeV in almost all cases. If we take ^{106}Pd, ^{108}Pd and ^{110}Pd for formula (17), we obtain 1.78, 2.21, and 2.62 MeV respectively: 99.9% of the energy goes into neutrons. The ^{3}He from reaction (12) and ^{3}T from reaction (13) have several MeV of energy. They bombard the other deuterium atoms and induce the d - d nuclear fusion reaction; ^{4}He, protons and neutrons are generated. The neutron energy is broadened from 14 to 17 MeV in this case. These mechanisms seem to give a solution to the questions of reaction products in cold fusion.

We would like to thank H. Tazima, T. Setoguchi, Y. Kasigawa, T. Shigemitu and S. Sawada for valuable discussions. We are grateful to M. Araki and J. Rothwell for strong support in our study. This work was supported in part by the NHE fund of the Institute for Applied Energy of NEDO.

References

1. H. Iwahara, T. Esaka, H. Uchida and N. Meda, *Solid State Ionics,* 3/4, 359 (1981).
2. H. Iwahara, H. Uchida, K. Kondo and K. Ogaki, *J. Electrochem Soc.*, 135, 529 (1988).
3. T. Yajima, K. Koide, K. Yamamoto and H. Iwahara, *Kenki Kagaku,* 58, 547 (1990).

Anomalous Isotopic Distribution in Palladium Cathode after Electrolysis

(From *Infinite Energy*, Vol. 2, No. 7, March/April 1996)

T. Mizuno - Dept. of Nuclear Eng., Fac. of Eng., Hokkaido Univ., Kita-ku, Sapporo, 060 Japan
T. Ohmori - Catalysis Research Center, Hokkaido Univ., Kita-ku, Sapporo, 060 Japan
M. Enyo - Hakodate National College of Technology, Tokura-cho, Hakodate, 042, Japan

Summary

It was confirmed by several analytic methods that reaction products with mass number ranging from 39 to 81, 104 to 136, and 177 to 208 are produced in palladium heavy water solution at high pressure, high temperature and high current density for one month. Isotopic distributions were radically different from the natural ones.

Introduction

Nuclear reactions in a solid electrode at ordinary temperature have been reported by many experimenters since 1989. However, this phenomenon is still not well accepted among researchers because of poor reproducibility and control. What is urgently needed now is to obtain precise and quantitative relationships between potential nuclear reactions and their corresponding reaction products. If nuclear reactions induced by electrochemical reaction occur in solid electrodes, there must be clear evidence such as the evolution of radioisotopes and radiation. Moreover, the evolution of the reaction products should be explained in terms of the nuclear mechanisms. In this work, evidence which indicates the occurrence of some nuclear reactions is presented, in the form of transmuted elements within the cathode and on the cathode surface. The anomalous isotopic distribution of these elements shows they do not come from contamination. For example, natural copper is 70% Cu^{63} and 30% Cu^{65}. But the copper found in the cathode was 100% Cu^{63}, with no detectable levels of Cu^{65}. Natural isotopic distribution varies by less than 0.001% for copper.

Experimental

Palladium rods used were of high purity (99.97% min.) supplied by Tanaka Noble Metals, Ltd. Impurities in the sample were as follows: B: 110 ppm, Si: 10, Ca: 9, Cr: 10, Cu: 6, Ti: 5, Ag: 44, Mg: 1, Pt: 20 and Au: 23. Nothing more was detected by atomic absorption photospectroscopy. Heavy water was supplied by Showa Denko, Ltd. It is 99.75% pure and includes 0.077 $\mu Ci/dm^3$ of tritium. The heavy water was purified once in a quartz glass distiller. Reagent grade lithium hydroxide was obtained from Merck, Ltd. and mixed with heavy water. Impurities in the reagent were specified as follows: Li_2CO_3: 2% max, Cl: 0.05%, Pb: 20 ppm, Ca: 200, Fe: 20, K: 200 and Na: 200. The anode and recombiner catalyst were, respectively, a high purity (99.99%) Pt plate and a Pt mesh. The Pt metal is specified to contain impurities as follows: Rh: 18 ppm, Si, Cr and Pd: 2 ppm, Au, Ag, B, Ca, Cu and Fe: less than 1 ppm. Other impurities were under the limits of detection.

Electrolysis was performed in a closed cell made of stainless steel. The cell inner wall was coated with 1 mm thick Teflon. The details have been described elsewhere.[1] Before the electrolyte was added to the Pd cell, it was pre-electrolyzed with Pt electrodes at 1 A and 150°C for 6 x 10^5s (7 days). Electrolysis experiments were performed at a current density of 0.2 A cm^2 or total current of 6.6 A at 105°C for 2.76 x 10^6 s (32 days). The sample electrodes were analyzed for element detection by energy dispersive, x-ray spectroscopy (EDX), Auger electron spectroscopy (AES) for depth profiles of the elements, secondary ion mass spectroscopy (SIMS) for isotopic distribution and electron probe microanalyzer (EPMA) for element distribution.

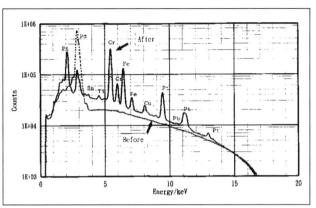

Figure 1. EDX spectra from the Pd rod before and after the electrolysis.

Results

Several elements were detected in the Pd electrode by the EDX method. Figure 1 shows typical results before and after electrolysis. The other elements were clearly seen. The amounts detected by EDX, AES and SIMS averaged together are shown in Figure 2. Amounts for all elements were calculated by the peak height of the estimate methods. Amounts were shown normalized with the Pd peak set as 100. Typical counts by EDX and SIMS ranged from 10^2 to 10^6 and were 10 to 100 times higher than the background counts. Thus, the pres-

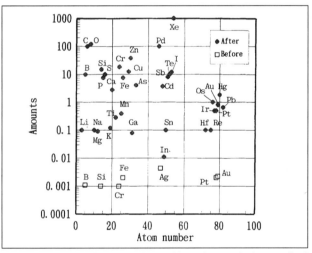

Figure 2. Amounts of elements observed by various methods, normalized with the Pd peak as 100.

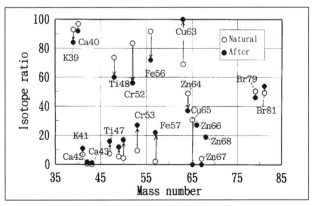

Figure 3. Shifts of isotopic distribution of reaction products as compared with natural isotopic distribution for mass numbers between 39 and 81.

ence of Ca, Ti, Cr, Mn, Fe, Co, Cu, Zn, Cd, Sn, Pt and Pb was confirmed. AES and SIMS measurements were also made after bombardment by Ar^+ or O^{2-} ions, thus removing surface layers, but the element concentrations at 1 [micron]μ below the electrode surface were almost the same as at the surface. Many holes and cracks were observed in the bulk layer, having 1 to 10 μ of opening size. The same elements, having almost the same concentration, were also found at the surface. These elements are mostly grouped in three ranges of atomic numbers: from 20 to 30; 46 to 54 and 72 to 82.

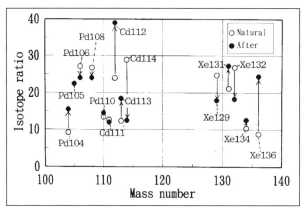

Figure 4. Shifts of isotopic distribution of reaction products as compared with natural isotopic distribution for mass numbers between 104 and 136.

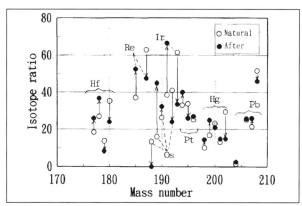

Figure 5. Shifts of isotopic distribution of reaction products as compared with natural isotopic distribution for mass numbers between 177 and 208.

The SIMS anaylsis showed other elements: As, Ga, Sb, Te, I, Hf, Re, Ir, Br and Xe. These elements, except Xe, are difficult to detect by AES and EDX because the peaks are very close to each other, or lower than the limits of detection. Xe is naturally difficult to detect by EDX because it is in the gas state. The SIMS count numbers ranged from 10^3 to 10^6 where the background counts were as low as ~10, so we have confidence in these results. In Figure 2 we show the peak intensities normalized with the peak of palladium as 100%. The intensity of Xe was 10 times larger than Pd; it may be that the gas was released by bombarding with O^{2-} ions which caused a temperature rise at the sample. Large differences in isotopic distributions compared with the natural distributions were observed by the SIMS method for Cu, Zn, Br, Xe, Pd, Cd, Hf, Re, Pt, Ir and Hg. Elements of mass number between 39 and 82 are shown in Figure 3; Cr, Fe and Cu showed large shifts in isotopic ratios. Especially notable was the fact that no ^{65}Cu peak was observed. Except for a few cases, in general the isotope abundances are higher for odd mass numbers and lower for even ones, as compared with the natural ratios. In Figure 4, for mass numbers between 100 and 140, Cd and Xe were shown to have large shifts in abundances. In Figure 5, for mass numbers between 172 and 208, large shifts were seen for Hf, Re, Ir, Os and Hg.

Generally speaking, heavier isotopes increased compared to the natural ratio, and lighter isotopes decreased. For example, ^{24}Mg went from 11% to 12%. This rule did not hold for some elements with few isotopes: ^{63}Cu increased while ^{65}Cu was absent. ^{47}Ti increased while ^{48}Ti decreased. The pattern is confusing for ^{111}Cd to ^{114}Cd: a slight increase, a giant increase, a large increase and compensating drop in heaviest isotope, number 114. Data from some elements are not shown in Figures 3 to 5 because their peaks overlapped with those of other elements, or because they showed only a small difference with natural abundance.

Neutron intensity and energy measurements were carried out simultaneously, in parallel. The neutron evolution rate was sporadic and weak, as previously reported,[2] with levels of ~0.4 counts per second. No gases such as He, O_2 and Ar were detected. Excess heat generation was less reproducible, varying from 10^5 to 10^7 joules.[3]

Discussion

Essentially the same phenomenon was confirmed five times with high reproducibility at high cathodic current density, above 0.2 cm². Current density ranged from 0.2 to 0.6 A/cm². Different isotope distributions were obtained depending on the current density. This will be described more fully in an upcoming paper. It can hardly be imagined that all of the elements found were impurities in electrolyte, electrode or cell. Even if we suppose that all impurities in the system accumulated in the cathode, the amount would be 10 to 100 times smaller than the total amount we detected. Furthermore, it is simply impossible to explain the shifts in the isotopic distribution. Hence, it must be concluded that some novel reactions occured, resulting in the reactants which were found abundant in the electrolyte and electrode material. We assume the cathode palladium was the starting material for these reactions, but it is possible that impurities and other cell componenets such as Li, D_2O, Pd, Pt, K, Na, Ca, B, C, Ag and Fe may have provided the starting material for the nuclear reactions.

The palladium surface became rough and porous after several weeks of electrolysis, probably due to hydrogen attack. The current may have increased in such roughened surface areas, which would in turn cause a larger reaction and a higher concentration of the reaction products. Enyo[4-6] reported that the effective hydrogen pressure at the hydrogen evolving electrode depends upon the hydrogen atom recombination process which follows the water discharge process. The division of the overpotential between these two steps may be important. It was suggested that at Pd electrodes in alkaline solution the effective hydrogen presssure may rise as high as 10^6 atm.[7,8] There may be further increases at local points on a heterogenous surface. One may even speculate that the hydrogen isotope nucleus sometimes closely approaches the medium nucleus.[9] An estimate by Nernst Equation indicates that 5×10^4 atm of pressure may be realized at 140 mV of overpotential at the electrolysis current density of 200 mA cm² on a flat palladium surface.[10] Furthermore, the pressure distribution depends on the roughness of the surface, because local current density and the partition of overpotential components may vary with roughness.

There are several reports[11-13] of evolution of elements by electrolysis. However, only a few [14,15] demonstrated shifts in isotopic abundance. For a gold electrode,[16] which also generated various elements by cathodic electrolysis, different isotopic distributions were seen. In this case also, the reaction sites were unevenly distributed on the surface. Typically, the active points may have occupied 10^{-6} cm² areas and numbered 10^4 to 10^5 per cm² at the surface. Thus, the current is likely to be concentrated at localized points 10 to 100 times higher than average. Such high pressure can induce neutrons to enter into heavy nuclei and successively form an unstable heavy nucleus.[17] If the reactions start from palladium as the electrode material, fusion and fission may take place simultaneously. Several possible reactions might be considered:

$$^{108}_{46}Pd + 2^2_1D \rightarrow ^{108}_{46}Pd^4_2 \rightarrow ^{116}_{48}Cd \, ,$$

$$^{108}_{46}Pd + 4^2_1D \rightarrow ^{108}_{46}Pd^8_4 \rightarrow ^{116}_{50}Sn \, ,$$

$$^{108}_{46}Pd + 8^2_1D \rightarrow ^{108}_{46}Pd^{16}_8 \rightarrow ^{124}_{54}Xe \, ,$$

$$^{102}_{46}Pd + 8^2_1D \rightarrow ^{102}_{46}Pd^{16}_8 \rightarrow ^{118}_{54}Xe \rightarrow ^{118}_{50}Sn + 4\,\beta^+ \, ,$$

$$^{104}_{46}Pd + 8^2_1D \rightarrow ^{104}_{46}Pd^{16}_8 \rightarrow ^{120}_{54}Xe \rightarrow ^{120}_{52}Te + 2\,\beta^+ \, ,$$

$$^{105}_{46}Pd + 8^2_1D \rightarrow ^{105}_{46}Pd^{16}_8 \rightarrow ^{121}_{54}Xe \rightarrow ^{121}_{51}Sb + 3\,\beta^+ \, ,$$

$$^{106}_{46}Pd + 8^2_1D \rightarrow ^{106}_{46}Pd^{16}_8 \rightarrow ^{122}_{54}Xe \rightarrow ^{122}_{52}Te + 2\,\beta^+ \, ,$$

Here, the bottom subscript at the right-hand side of the intermediates represents the proton number and the top superscript represents the total nuclear number which is connected with the nucleus as the hollow atom. It can be assumed that these particles will stay in a stable orbit according to their quantum spin number as the same concept with electron orbits. The connecting nuclei are caught into medium nuclei by the force of high external pressure.

Other reactions have to be assumed because many light elements were observed. They may be as follows:

$$^{102}_{46}Pd + 2D \rightarrow 2^{51}_{23}V + ^4_2He$$

$$\rightarrow ^{50}_{22}Ti + ^{52}_{24}Cr + ^4_2He$$

$$\rightarrow ^{48}_{20}Ca + ^{57}_{26}Fe + He$$

Generally, one can write the fission reactions as follows:

$$_{46}Pd + 2D \rightarrow _nA + _{46-n}B + He$$

In the case of platinum deposited from the aug. electrode to the Pd electrode surface, some reactions may be involved, such as :

$$^{196}_{78}Pt + 2^2_1D \rightarrow ^{196}_{78}Pt^4_2 \rightarrow ^{200}_{80}Hg \, ,$$

$$^{198}_{78}Pt + 4^2_1D \rightarrow ^{198}_{78}Pt^8_4 \rightarrow ^{206}_{82}Pb \, ,$$

They may induce fission reactions as follows:

$$^{194}_{78}Pt + 2^2_1D \rightarrow ^{136}_{54}Xe + ^{58}_{26}Fe + ^4_2He$$

$$^{195}_{78}Pt + 2^2_1D \rightarrow ^{136}_{54}Xe + ^{59}_{26}Fe + ^4_2He$$

$$^{59}_{27}Co + \beta^-$$

$$^{196}_{78}Pt + 2^2_1D \rightarrow ^{136}_{54}Xe + ^{60}_{26}Fe + ^4_2He$$

$$^{60}_{28}Ni + 2\beta^-$$

Atomic numbers of 20, 28, 50 and 82 are called magic numbers. Here, $^{136}_{54}Xe$ nuclei are abnormally increased and hence the number of neutrons changes to magic number 82 and especially stable nuclei are selectively produced. In this way, the isotopic distributions of the products after electrolysis can be explained in terms of the difference of binding energy of the nuclei.

It must be admitted that these reactions may have no solid, detailed theoretical basis yet, but in broad terms this can explain most of the elements which were observed. One may also imagine that as such transmutation reactions were presumably taking place during the electrochemical process, they are likely to be connected with other phenomena such as hydrogen embrittlement and local corrosion.

Conclusion

Anomalous evolution of various elements in palladium electrodes was confirmed after high current density cathodic electrolysis under high temperature and pressure for a long time. The following conclusions were drawn:

1) The mass number of the evolved elements were distributed roughly in three groups: 20 to 28, 46 to 54, and 72 to 82, with the amounts, respectively, >50%, 10% and <5%, compared to palladium.

2) These evolved elements were found on the surface and also in the bulk of the electrode, but in amounts 10 to 100 times smaller than on the surface.

3) Many evolved elements accumulated in holes and cracks on the electrode which formed during electrolysis.

4) Some of the evolved elements have isotopic distributions drastically different from natural ones, especially for Cu, Ze, Br, Xe, Pd, Cd, Hf, Re, Pt, Ir and Hg.

5) Gaseous Xe was noteworthy because it was so abundant. Xenon is particularly unlikely to be a contaminant because metals do not absorb noble gases and because the cathode was degassed in a vacuum at 473°K for 20 hours.

6) The elements in the bulk layer changed in concentration with depth and showed shifts of isotopic distribution.

7) Light elements such as O, C, Ca, Na, Mg and Al showed small isotopic shifts.

8) Ni and Co were also confirmed but their isotopic distribution could not be measured because their SIMS peaks overlapped with those of other elements.

9) The isotopic distributions of Pd and Pt were also shifted.

10) We conclude that nuclear reactions must have occurred during the electrochemical process.

Acknowledgement

The authors acknowledge financial support from the Association of New Hydrogen Energy in Japan.

References

1. Tadahiko Mizuno, Tadashi Akimoto, Kazuhisa Azumi and Michio Enyo, "Diffusion Rate of Deuterium in Pd During Cathodic Charging," *Denki Kagaku*, Vol. 60, No. 5, p. 405 (1992).
2. Tadahiko Mizuno, Tadashi Akimoto and Norio Sato, "Neutron Evolution from Annealed Palladium Cathode in LiOD-D_2O Solution," *Denki Kagaku*, Vol. 57, No. 7, p. 742 (1989).
3. Tadahiko Mizuno, Tadashi Akimoto, Kazuhisa Azumi and Norio Sato, "Tritium Evolution During Cathodic Polarization of Palladium Electrode in D_2O Solution," *Denki Kagaku*, Vol. 59. No. 9, p. 789 (1991).

4. Tadanori Maoka and Michio Enyo, "Hydrogen Absorption by Palladium Electrode Polarized in Sulfuric Acid Solution Containing Surface Active Substances: II," *Electrochimica Acta,* Vol. 26, No. 5, pp. 615-619 (1981).

5. Tadanori Maoka and Michio Enyo, "The Overpotential Components on the Palladium Hydrogen Electrode," *J. Electroanal. Chem.,* No. 108. pp. 277-292 (1980).

6. Michio Enyo, "Kinetics of the Elementary Steps of the Hydrogen Electrode Reaction on Pd in Acidic Solution," *J. Electroanal. Chem.,* No. 134, pp. 75-86 (1982).

7. Tadahiko Mizuno and Michio Enyo, "Sorption of Hydrogen On and In Hydrogen-Absorbing Metals in Electrochemical Environments," *Modern Aspects of Electrochemistry,* Vol. 30 (1996).

8. M. Enyo and P.C. Biswas, "Hydrogen Absorption in Pd Electrode in Alkaline Solutions," *J. Electroanal. Chem.,* No. 335, pp. 309-319 (1992).

9. C.E. Rolfs and W.S. Rodney, "Cauldron in the Cosmos," *Theoretical Astrophysics Series,* The University of Chicago Press, 96-112 (1988).

10. Moshe H. Mintz, "Mixed Mechanisms Controlling Hydrogen-Interface Mechanisms," *J. Alloys and Compunds,* No. 176, pp. 77-87 (1191).

11. J. O'M. Bockris and R. Sundaresan, "Electrochemistry, Tritium and Transmutation," (Table 2) *Cold Fusion Source Book* (ed. H. Fox), International Symposium on Cold Fusion and Advanced Energy Sources, Minsk, Belarus, May 1994.

12. Y. Kucherov, A. Karabut, I. Savvatimova, "Calorimetric and Nuclear Products Measurements at Glow-Discharge in Deuterium," Scientific Industrial Association, LUCH Prodolsk, Moscow Region, Russian Federation (1995); reviewed by M. Swartz, *Cold Fusion Times,* Vol. 1, No. 4, p. 10.

13. M.I. Martinov, A.I. Meldianov and A.M. Cherepovski, "Investigation of Anomalous Nuclear Events in Metals Saturated with Deuterium," Cold Nuclear Fusion, Center of Intersectorial Science, Engineering and Venture, Non-Conventional Technologies, Moscow, 84-91 (1995); abstracts review; *Fusion Facts,* Vol. 5, No. 5, November 20, 1995.

14. Tadayoshi Ohmori and Michio Enyo, "Excess Heat Evolution During Electrolysis of H_2O with Nickel, Gold and Tin Cathodes," *Fusion Technology,* Vol. 24, pp. 293-295 (1993).

15. R.T. Bush and R.D. Eagleton, *Frontiers of Cold Fusion,* Universal Academy Press, p. 405-408 (1993).

16. T. Mizuno, T. Ohmori, K. Kurokawa, T. Akimoto, M. Kitaichi, M. Enyo, "Anomalous isotopes found in cathode precipitate after electrolysis," Denkikagaku oyobi kougaku buturi kagaku, Vol. 65, No. 11 (1996) 1160-1165.

17. A.C. Mueller and B.M. Sherrill, "Nuclei at the Limits of Particle Stability," *Annul. Rev. Nucl.* Part. Sci., pp. 529-583 (1993).

GLOSSARY

accelerator See ion accelerator.

adsorption absorption, desorption; Adsorption occurs when a solid surface attracts molecules of gas or liquid. A liquid may be adsorbed onto a surface, and then absorbed into the bulk of the solid material. Desorption is the opposite of adsorption; *i.e.,* the removal of gas from a surface.

AES auger electron spectroscopy. See mass spectroscope.

alpha particle, alpha decay See radioactive decay.

amp measure of electrical current. One amp equals one coulomb of charge per second.

angstrom unit measure of distance = 10^{-10} meters

anode the positive electrode in an electrochemical cell, which attracts oxygen (see electrode; electrolysis)

atom atomic nucleus, chemical versus nuclear reactions
The smallest unit of an element, consisting of a positively charged nucleus surrounded by a cloud of negatively charged electrons. Most of the mass of an atom is concentrated in the nucleus, which is made up of protons and neutrons. Chemical reactions affect only the electrons, leaving the nucleus unchanged. Nuclear reactions affect the nucleus, changing the atom into a different element or isotope.

Auger electron spectroscope (AES) See mass spectroscope.

autoradiograph an image produced on photographic film by a radioactive substance placed in close contact with the film; Autoradiographs are good for detecting cumulative low level radioactivity. During cold fusion experiments, sometimes minute amounts of the metal in a cathode will transmute to another radioactive element or isotope. These radioactive species can be detected by leaving the cathode on unexposed film for hours or days and then developing the film. They can be detected by other means as well, but this is a particularly sensitive and reliable method, and it shows the uneven distribution of the radioactive elements in tiny "hot spots" on the metal.

beta particle, beta decay See radioactive decay.

BF3 detector a nuclear measurement instrument that detects neutrons; Neutrons hit the boron nucleus in BF_3 producing ultimately an electrical signal proportional to the number of neutrons.

calibrate In the first phase of an experiment, an instrument is calibrated by measuring a known quantity, or by comparing it against a standard, higher quality instrument. For example, a thermometer might be calibrated by exposing it to an ice slurry, which is at $0\,°C$ (by definition) and boiling water at $100\,°C$. Or, it might be calibrated by placing it in a beaker of warm, stirred water along with two other high quality thermometers. As the water cools, the temperatures shown on all three thermometers are noted, and a correction factor is determined for the target thermometer.

A calorimeter might be calibrated by placing an electric heater in the sample chamber, and running 1 watt through the heater for several hours, then 2 watts, 3, 4 and 5 watts. At each power level the calorimeter stabilizes at a particular temperature, when the heat going into the water is balanced by losses out of the calorimeter walls to the surroundings. Suppose you find that at 1 watt the temperature settles 2.4°C above the surrounding temperature; at 2 watts, 4.8°C; at 3 watts, 7.2°C and so on. You graph these temperatures to make a calibration curve, and you determine the calibration constant is 2.4°C per watt, or 0.42 watts per degree Celsius. Later, a test device placed in the calorimeter raises the temperature 5.1°C. You know that the test device is producing 2.1 watts of heat.

This method of calibration works because the electric power consumed by the heater in the chamber can be measured with great precision, and the power remains stable over time. The calibration will be less reliable with poor quality meters and a low quality power supply that produces fluctuating power. The greatest difficulty in calibrating a calorimeter is often noise introduced by changes in the temperature of the surroundings.

In a cold fusion experiment calibration and other testing of the instruments may take days, weeks, several months, or years.

calorie   The energy required to raise one gram of water by one degree Celsius. This equals approximately 4.19 joules (watt-seconds). Note that a "dietary" or "large calorie" equals 1,000 calories. The energy content of food when oxidized in the body is measured in large calories.

calorimeter   an instrument that measures the heat generated by an exothermic process, or the heat absorbed by an endothermic process; Conventional, old-fashioned calorimeters surround the sample with water. The sample heats (or cools) and the water temperature rises (or falls). The mass of water and the temperature indicate how much heat energy was produced. In a modern electronic Seebeck envelope calorimeter, the sample is surrounded by panels containing hundreds of thermocouples connected in series—a thermopile. The net output from all thermocouples together indicates the amount of heat evolving from the sample.

catalyst   a substance that modifies and usually increases the rate of a reaction without being consumed in the process; In a closed cold fusion cell, platinum mesh or beads are often used as a catalyst that cause the free deuterium gas to recombine with oxygen at low temperatures. See Recombination.

cathode   the negative electrode in an electrochemical cell, which attracts hydrogen.; (See electrode; electrolysis.) In the original Fleischmann-Pons cold fusion experiment, the cathode is made of palladium, which absorbs the hydrogen.

ceramic proton conductor   a solid state electrolyte used in some high temperature cold fusion experiments

cosmic rays ionizing radiation from outer space, consisting mainly of protons, alpha particles (helium nuclei), and other atomic nuclei, plus some high-energy electrons

coulomb barrier attractive or repulsive electrostatic force from a nucleus; The coulomb barrier keeps positively charged atomic nuclei apart, making it highly unlikely that two atoms will fuse when they happen to hit one another. Many people have argued that cold fusion cannot be real because electrolysis does not exert enough force for a significant number of atoms to overcome the coulomb barrier and fuse together.

D-D, D-T fusion D-D refers to deuterium - deuterium fusion, in which two deuterium nuclei come together. In high temperature plasma fusion, this reaction has two different possible outcomes, with equal likelihood. It might result in a helium-3 nucleus plus a neutron, or it might result in a tritium nucleus and a proton. Cold fusion occasionally produces tritium and neutrons, but never in the proportions seen in plasma fusion. D-T refers to deuterium - tritium fusion. With plasma fusion this is easier to achieve than D-D and it produces more energy for each reaction.

deuterium, tritium Deuterium is heavy hydrogen. Ordinary, light hydrogen atoms consist of one proton and one electron. A heavy hydrogen atom has one proton and one neutron in the nucleus, and an electron. In ordinary water, approximately one hydrogen atom in every 6,200 is heavy hydrogen.

A tritium atom nucleus has one proton and two neutrons. Tritium is a radioactive isotope, with a half-life of 12.3 years. There is practically no measurable tritium in ordinary air and water.

Deuterium and tritium are isotopes of hydrogen.

Water made with deuterium (D_2O) is called heavy water. In contrast, ordinary water is sometimes referred to as "light water" but it actually contains one part in 6,200 heavy water. This ratio is the same in all natural water everywhere on earth, in ice, water, and steam.

deuteride metal that has absorbed deuterium. See hydride.

deuteron a deuterium ion; a proton and a neutron

EDX energy dispersive X-ray spectroscopy; See mass spectroscope.

electrolysis, electrode, electrolyte Electrolysis is the passing of an electric current from one electrode to another through a liquid, which is called the electrolyte. Electrolysis breaks apart the molecules of liquid into positively and negatively charged ions. The positively charged ions are attracted to the negative electrode (the cathode), and the negative ions are attracted to the positive electrode (the anode). A water molecule consists of two hydrogen atoms and one oxygen atom. When it is electrolyzed, it breaks apart. The hydrogen atoms are positively charged so they are attracted to the cathode, while the free oxygen atom is pulled to the anode. Another way to express this is to say that oxidation occurs at the anode and reduction occurs at the cathode.

electron volt (eV) the energy gained by an electron in passing from a point of low potential to a point one volt higher in potential, abbreviated eV; kilo and mega electron volts are abbreviated KeV and MeV; Chemical reactions typically produce a fraction of 1 eV per atom, or at most 4 or 5 eV. Nuclear reactions produce MeV levels of energy per atom. An electron volt equals 1.6 x 10^{-19} joules.

energy versus power Energy is heat, or the capacity to do work measured, for example, in joules. Power is the instantaneous measure of energy per unit of time. In other words, at a given moment the power level might be 10 watts—10 joules per second. When this power continues steadily for 20 seconds, it adds up to 200 joules of energy.

Power is measured in watts; energy is measured in joules. One joule is one watt continued for one second; a 100-watt lightbulb generates 6,000 joules of light and heat per minute (100 watts x 60 seconds). Large amounts of energy are sometimes measured in kilowatt-hours (1,000 watts continued for 1 hour, or 3.6 million joules).

EPMA electron probe microanalyzer; See mass spectroscope.

excess heat heat generated by a chemical or nuclear reaction inside a calorimeter over and above the heat provided by external sources; In a cold fusion experiment where electrolysis consumes 4 watts but the cell produces 5 watts, the extra watt is excess heat. At first you cannot tell whether it is caused by a chemical or a nuclear reaction. If it continues for a long time, adding up to a great deal more energy than chemical reaction might produce, and if you find no indication of a chemical reaction after the experiment terminates, you know it must have been caused by a nuclear reaction instead (or by some unknown energy-tapping process much more energetic than chemical).

exothermic, endothermic An exothermic chemical or nuclear reaction produces net energy. An endothermic reaction consumes net energy. In a cold fusion cell, when the palladium initially absorbs a great deal of hydrogen or deuterium to form a hydride, this is an endothermic chemical process that absorbs heat and cools the surroundings. After the current is turned off, much of the hydrogen gradually escapes from the cathode, which is an exothermic reaction. The two cancel out one another; the heat absorbed by the first reaction equals the heat generated by the second if all of the hydrogen leaves the palladium. (Actually, much of the hydrogen usually remains; it is difficult to drive it all out.) These chemical reactions absorb or produce much less heat than the nuclear reactions considered to explain cold fusion.

fission, fusion Fission is the breaking apart of heavy element atomic nuclei to form lighter elements. Fusion means building up heavier elements by combining lighter ones together. When elements heavier than iron fission, they release energy. Fissioning elements lighter than iron consumes energy. Fusion is the opposite: the lighter the element, the more energy produced during fusion. Fusing the lightest element, hydrogen, produces the most energy of any nuclear process. This energy drives the stars.

Fission and fusion both result in transmutation: changing one element or isotope into another.

gamma ray electromagnetic radiation emitted by radioactive decay or other very high energy processes; Gamma rays have between 10 KeV and 100 MeV of energy and beyond.

heat-after-death In some cold fusion experiments, the palladium cathode has remained hot long after electrolysis has been turned off and the cell should have cooled. Pons and Fleischmann first reported this and called it "heat-after-death."

heavy water, light water See deuterium.

helium the second lightest element, with two isotopes: helium-3, with two protons and one neutron, which is stable, and helium-4 with two protons and two neutrons, which is also stable; Helium-4 is the by-product of many nuclear reactions. There is good evidence that the cold fusion reaction produces it, and some evidence that some cold fusion reactions produce helium-3.

hydride a metal that has absorbed hydrogen; A deuteride is a metal that has absorbed deuterium. More generally, this means a compound of hydrogen with a more electropositive element or group.

ion an electrically charged atom or group of atoms; a positive ion is an atom that has been stripped of one or more outer electrons; a negative ion has extra electrons

ion accelerator An ion accelerator creates ions, then pushes them to high speeds in a vacuum chamber—a tube—by creating a difference of potential from one section of the tube to the next. The ions strike a target at the end of the tube. In a small accelerator the ions may move at 8,000 km per second, or 3% of the speed of light. A linear accelerator, like the one on the campus of Hokkaido University, pushes the ions once, down a straight tube, directly into the target. A cyclic accelerator pushes the ions around in circles many times, until they reach a high speed and escape the confining magnetic field. The power of an accelerator is measured by the amount of kinetic energy each atom accumulates before it strikes the target, measured in electron volts (eV).

Small accelerators are incorporated in many scientific instruments, like the SIMS mass spectroscope (see), and the neutron generator Mizuno used when he was working on his graduate thesis.

isotope, isotopic ratio An atom with the same number of protons but a different number of neutrons. One element may have several isotopes. For example, an atom of copper always has 29 protons, but some copper atoms have 34 neutrons and some have 36, which makes some copper atoms heavier than others. The two isotopes of copper have atomic masses of 63 (29+34) and 65 (29+36). These isotopes are designated copper-63 (^{63}Cu) and copper-65 (^{65}Cu). Some elements, like gold, have only one isotope. Most isotopes have the same gross chemical properties, but subtle differences in behavior have been observed, such as better conductivity with different isotopes of iron. There may be many more undiscovered differences between isotopes, but the subject has not been researched in detail because it is difficult and expensive to separate out isotopes and prepare pure mono-isotopic samples.

In nature, on earth, different isotopes of an element are found in different ratios, and these ratios are fixed. For example, 69% of copper is copper-63, 31% is copper-65. With other elements the isotopic ratios are more extreme: Oxygen-16 is 99.762% of all atoms; oxygen-17 is 0.038% and oxygen-18 is 0.200%. When an element is found with unnatural isotopic ratios (also called unnatural isotopic distribution), it can only have two origins:

isotope, isotopic ratio *continued*

1. It might be man-made, using a chemical or physical separation technique. Ontario Hydro produces purified heavy water for CANDU fission reactors. Uranium isotopes are purified to make atomic bombs.

2. It might come from a nuclear reaction, in which one element is transmuted into one or more other elements.

Cold fusion causes changes in isotopic ratios. After his proton conductors produced excess heat, Mizuno examined them and found monoisotopic copper; all copper-63, with no copper-65. There is no evidence that cold fusion is anything like an electrochemical isotopic separation technique. The copper-65 was not separated out and pushed to the side; it was not found anywhere in the sample. Cold fusion apparently created it out of some other element.

joule   a measure of energy; one watt of power maintained for one second; 1 calorie = 4.19 joules. In U.S. industry, energy is sometimes measured in British Thermal Units (BTU), the energy required to raise one pound of water by one degree Fahrenheit. 1 btu = 1,055 joules.

joule heating   heat created by a device that passes a current through a resistance

KeV   kilo electron volt; See electron volt.

linear accelerator   See ion accelerator.

mass spectroscope, mass spectroscopy   an instrument that reveals the elements within a sample, aligning them in a spectrum from lightest to heaviest; The spectrum is divided into atomic mass units (amu). A sample containing mostly gold, mass 197, will show a large peak at 197 with smaller peaks for each contaminant. A sensitive instrument will reveal individual isotopes. A less sensitive instrument will blur together isotopes and isobars, that is, isotopes of different elements with same atomic weight, where the lower numbered element has many neutrons and the next higher element happens to have few neutrons.

Several different types of mass spectroscopes are available. Each has various pros and cons. For example, some cannot easily distinguish between molecules and atoms with very close atomic weights. Some cannot easily distinguish between a deuterium molecule and a helium atom (4.02820 amu versus 4.00260 amu). To be sure a transmutation result is real, an experimenter must use several types, confirming similar results with each. Mizuno sent samples of transmuted cathodes to four industrial laboratories in blind tests, and these laboratories each used two or three spectroscope types.

For analysis within Hokkaido University, Mizuno uses in-house **SIMS, EPMA** and **EDX** mass spectroscopes:

SIMS stands for secondary ion mass spectrometry. In this instrument, the sample is bombarded with highly charged oxygen or other ions, which free up and ionize the atoms in the surface. The ions pass through a magnetic field which bends the trajectory of lighter isotopes more than heavier ones, producing a spectrum. A SIMS spectroscope can have a tiny, highly focused beam which examines one small area of a sample surface rather than looking at the entire sample. This will reveal an inhomogeneous distribution of elements. When the ion beam is held at one spot on the sample for a long time, it gradually eats away at the surface (sputters it), revealing lower levels of atoms. Eventually this destroys the sample. Other methods of spectroscopy are non-destructive, and some reveal the distribution of elements and isotopes for the entire sample simultaneously, like NAA (neutron activation analysis).

EPMA electron probe microanalyzer; With EPMA, a stream of electrons strikes the target giving rise to X-rays. The X-ray energy levels are measured to determine the elements in the sample.

EDX energy dispersive X-ray spectroscopy, similar to an EPMA.

AES auger electron spectroscope; The sample is bombarded with x-rays, and the kinetic energy of the electrons emitted from it is measured.

MeV million (mega) electron volts; See electron volt.

milliamp one thousandth of an amp; See amp.

moderator a substance such as water, graphite or paraffin, which slows down or stops neutrons emitted by nuclear reactions; Mizuno used a moderator to prevent neutrons from external sources from corrupting his experiment.

NAA neutron activation analysis; See mass spectroscope.

neutron a neutral (uncharged) particle in the nucleus of all atoms except light hydrogen; A neutron weighs almost exactly as much as a proton.

neutron counter an instrument that counts neutrons and measures their energy spectrum; Mizuno used a liquid scintillation detector.

neutron generator, neutron source a device that generates neutrons on demand; In his early research, Mizuno used an old neutron generator that worked by accelerating deuterium ions into a metal target. The target generated neutrons. A neutron source is a sample of radioactive material that continually generates neutrons.

overpotential (overvoltage) In an electrochemical cell, it takes a certain level of voltage to break apart the molecules of the electrolyte. Any voltage above this is called the overvoltage or overpotential. Higher overpotential puts greater pressure on the hydrogen or deuterium forced into the cathode.

palladium, platinum these precious metals have similar properties and the ores are often found together; Palladium absorbs a large amount of hydrogen, so it is used in hydrogen filters, hydrogenation catalysts, and cold fusion cathodes. Platinum is often used for the anode in a cold fusion cell, or as the cathode in a control run, that is, in a test which is not supposed to produce excess heat, used to calibrate the equipment in preparation for a test with palladium.

plasma atoms broken into protons, charged atoms, neutrons, and electrons in a highly ionized gas-like state; Electrically, a plasma is neutral.

proton a positively charged particle in the nucleus of an atom

proton conductor a solid state electrolyte used by Dr. Mizuno and others in solid state, gas phase cold fusion experiments

radioactive decay In radioactive decay, a particle is emitted from the nucleus of an atom, and the atom converts from one element to another. There are three forms of naturally occurring (spontaneous decay) in which atoms convert themselves with no outside influence.

An alpha particle is emitted by one form of natural radioactive decay. The alpha particle is a helium nucleus: two protons and two neutrons. Alpha particles are positively charged. Alpha decay occurs with heavier elements, those above the middle of the periodic table. Two other forms of radioactive decay occur with uranium and heavier elements: spontaneous fission and beta decay. Spontaneous fission occurs when a heavy element splits into two nearly equal fragments, forming two atoms of lighter elements. Beta decay involves electrons emitted from or captured by a nucleus. Since electrons are much lighter than protons and neutrons, the mass of the atom changes only a little; the mass number remains the same, but the element is transmuted into another element. For example, tritium (super-heavy hydrogen) consists of a proton and two neutrons, mass number 3. When tritium undergoes beta decay, a neutron converts into a proton, one electron is emitted, and the atom transmutes from hydrogen into helium-3 (two protons, one neutron), still with mass number 3. There are three kinds of beta decay:

1. Negative electron beta decay, in which a neutron converts to a proton, an electron is emitted, and the element transmutes to the next higher element.

2. Positron emission, in which a proton converts into a neutron and a positive electron (a positron, an antimatter electron) is emitted, and the element transmutes to the next lower element.

3. Electron capture, also called K-capture. An electron from the lowest orbit (the K shell orbit) is captured by a proton, which converts to a neutron, and the element transmutes to the next lower element.

These are natural forms of radioactive decay, meaning the atoms change by themselves, in contrast to nuclear changes which occur when a mass of material is gathered inside a reactor or a nuclear bomb, or when neutrons from a reactor bombard material. In this case, neutrons from one reaction cause another reaction in another atom.

recombination, recombiner Electrolysis breaks apart water molecules into hydrogen and oxygen. It breaks heavy water into deuterium (heavy hydrogen) and oxygen. In a cold fusion experiment, some deuterium is absorbed by the cathode, but most of it forms gas on the cathode which bubbles out of the electrolyte, along with the oxygen gas bubbling off the anode. When a cell is open to the atmosphere, the gas drifts into the air, where the free deuterium eventually combines with oxygen to form heavy water again. This process is called recombination. In a closed cell the gas is trapped, so it must be immediately recombined to form heavy water, or pressure will build up and the cell will explode. Free oxygen and hydrogen gas will not spontaneously recombine at room temperature. They will explode when exposed to a spark or flame; that is, they will recombine suddenly and spontaneously. A cold fusion cell might be equipped with a spark plug in the head space to ensure that all free deuterium gas recombines, but this would be clumsy and it would affect the calorimetry. Instead, to ensure smooth, instant recombination, closed cells are equipped with catalytic recombiners, which are usually mesh or beads made of platinum. When deuterium gas and oxygen come in contact with the platinum, they recombine at room temperature. The recombiner must be carefully selected and placed in the cell in the correct orientation, at the proper distance above the electrolyte in the cell head space. If it becomes covered with recombined water, it may stop functioning, and cause an explosion. A recombiner failure was a contributing factor to the tragic accident at SRI on January 2, 1992, which killed Andrew Riley. (See Chapter 4.) Mizuno experienced problems with his recombiner. In one experiment, small amounts of gas repeatedly built up and exploded, jarring the cell and causing large pressure changes.

Recombination was a major bugbear early in the history of cold fusion. Marginal excess heat results with an open cell might be caused by unforeseen recombination. Suppose the input power to a heavy water cell is 1 amp, 2 volts. This equals 3 watts of input, but only 0.5 watts of the power converts to heat energy in the cell. The rest is carried out of the cell in the form of free oxygen and deuterium gas, which will eventually recombine and heat the atmosphere. So the experimenter would expect to see only 0.5 watts of heating. However, suppose something in the cell caused the free gas to recombine. For example, suppose a platinum anode was mounted above the cathode, instead of side-by-side, which is proper configuration. Some deuterium bubbles would drift up, mix in with the oxygen, touch the platinum, and recombine. The flow of gas leaving the cell would be less than the experimenter expected, and heat generation would be greater than predicted. If the experimenter was extraordinarily unobservant, and he failed to note that the gas flow was below the expected level, he might think that the cell was producing excess heat. In the worst case the gas flow might drop to zero, and 2 watts of heat would be generated, which would look like 1.5 watts of excess heat. This is farfetched, because it is hard to believe an experimenter would fail to note that bubbles have stopped emerging from the electrolyte. These bubbles are readily observable, like the fizz in a soft drink.

Even today, some skeptics claim that recombination can account for all positive results, but this is impossible. Many cells are closed and others employ gas flowmeters to confirm that the expected level of gas evolution is occurring. Furthermore, many experiments produce more energy than a recombination error could introduce. In our example with 1 amp, 2 volts, some cells will output 3 or more watts, significantly more than the largest possible 2 watt recombination error.

scintillation counter a nuclear measurement instrument that detects particles or energetic electromagnetic radiation by sensing the emission of light flashes that are produced in its solid, liquid, or gaseous medium

SIMS secondary ion mass spectrometry; See mass spectroscope.

stoichiometric Stoichiometry, in chemistry, means the proportions in which elements or compounds react, based on the laws of conservation of mass and energy. A stoichiometric mixture of elements is one which will form a compound with no material left over. Each material is present in exactly the correct mass to form the final product. For example, if a test tube has one part oxygen to two parts hydrogen, it will form water with no oxygen or hydrogen left over.

Tafel equations In electrochemical systems in which current is flowing, a semi-empirical relationship is obtained. In many cases, current and voltage increase together, with voltage (overpotential) logarithmically dependent on current density. This is shown as follows in what is known as the Tafel equation:

(overpotential) = a ± b log I / I_o, where:

a and b are constants, I electric current, I_o units of electric current

temperature versus power When a body that is producing energy is placed in a calorimeter, the temperature of the water in the calorimeter will rise above ambient. How much it rises depends upon mass of water, the emissivity and heat transfer coefficient of the cell wall. In most calorimeters there is no fixed relationship between temperature and power. Theoretically, a 1 gram mass of water in a "perfectly insulated vessel" will rise one degree Celsius for every 4.2 joules of energy input, but in the real world there is no such thing as a perfectly insulated vessel. The calorimeters Mizuno uses are not intended to be well insulated. Instead, they depend upon a uniform, predictable heat loss from the cell, and a calibration curve established before the experiment begins (see calibration).

thermocouple two dissimilar metals bonded together that generate a small voltage that is dependent on the temperature; Thus voltage measurement in a thermocouple can be used to measure temperature.

thermal neutron a neutron emitted by a nuclear reaction which has been slowed down until it is in thermal equilibrium with the surrounding media; That is, until it has the same kinetic energy as the other particles in the media. Also called a "slow neutron." Neutrons are slowed by a moderator; that is, a block of paraffin or some other material that impedes the neutron (see moderator).

transmutation the conversion of one element into another by fission (breaking apart the atomic nuclei) or fusion (bringing together and combining nuclei)

tritium a hydrogen atom with two neutrons in its nucleus; Tritium is radioactive (see hydrogen).

volt a measure of electrical potential—analogous to water pressure in a waterline; Direct current electric power is measured in volts multiplied by amperes. Increasing either will increase the amount of work the electricity can do. In a rough analogy to a river pushing a water wheel to perform work, voltage is the height the water falls, and amperage is the volume of water.

watt (electrical, thermal) a measure of power; In direct current electricity, watts = volts x amps. A thermal watt is the level of heat production per unit time that you get from a heater that consumes one watt of electric power.

X-rays electromagnetic radiation that is produced when high-energy electrons bombard metals

INDEX *

*Index includes text only. Timeline, glossary and appendices are not indexed.

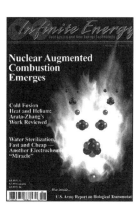